GLENCOE LANGUAGE ARTS

SPELLING POWER

TEACHER ANNOTATED EDITION

GRADE 9

Glencoe
McGraw-Hill

New York, New York   Columbus, Ohio   Woodland Hills, California   Peoria, Illinois

Glencoe/McGraw-Hill

A Division of The McGraw·Hill Companies

Send all inquiries to:
Glencoe/McGraw-Hill
8787 Orion Place
Columbus, Ohio 43240

ISBN 0-07-826245-3

Printed in the United States of America

5 6 7 8 9 10 024 10 09 08

CONTENTS

TEACHING AND ASSESSING SPELLING

By providing spelling exercises, skills practice, reviews, and quizzes, this *Spelling Power* workbook gives students the practice they need to improve their spelling and writing ability and to expand their vocabulary.

The spelling words, patterns, and concepts taught throughout *Spelling Power* have been carefully selected on the basis of current research in word study. Sources such as *The Reading Teacher's Book of Lists*, authored by readability experts Edward Bernard Fry, Jacqueline E. Kress, and Dona Lee Fountoukidis, and *The Living Word*, a national vocabulary inventory by Dale Edgar and Joseph O'Rourke, identify words students typically misspell at each grade level, so the words selected for study in this workbook are developmentally appropriate. They also reflect the varied interests and vocabulary of today's students.

Lesson Structure

Each spelling lesson, which focuses on a single spelling pattern or concept, begins with a **Word Bank**–a list of words that demonstrate the pattern and exceptions to it if necessary. (A complete alphabetized list of spelling words may be found at the end of this workbook.) Following the Word Bank is an explanation of **Key Concepts,** which provides spelling instruction and discussion by applying the pattern or concept to the words in the Word Bank. Four exercises–**Spelling Practice, Spelling in Context, Proofreading Practice,** and **Spelling Application**–provide students with a variety of ways to apply what they have learned in the lesson: writing the words, using them in the context of sentences, recognizing and correcting them as they proofread, and applying the lesson's spelling pattern or concept to new words that follow the same pattern.

The structure of the lessons enables students to monitor their own progress. Students having difficulty completing an exercise may refer to the Key Concepts discussion, review and relearn the spelling pattern or concept, and then return to the exercise.

Assessment

This *Spelling Power* workbook may be used for systematic spelling instruction, and frequent assessment is an integral part of that instruction. If you evaluate students' abilities before, during, and after a lesson or group of lessons, you can adjust your teaching to maximize classroom time. In addition, assessments provide students with real learning opportunities. Only through assessment can students discover what they already know, what they've mastered, and what they need to learn to ensure future success.

The Oral Quizzes and Reviews provided in *Spelling Power* may be used in a variety of ways to assess student achievement. The following discussion provides several suggestions for how and when to administer them.

Pretest   Before beginning a lesson, conduct a pretest to determine whether students already know some or all of the material and then set a course for your instruction on the basis of student performance. To conduct a pretest for any lesson in *Spelling Power*, choose from the following strategies:

- Read each word in the Word Bank aloud, giving students time to spell the word on paper.
- Read the words listed in the Spelling Application exercise, which presents additional words that follow the same pattern taught in the lesson.
- Administer the Oral Quiz for the lesson, which may be found in this Annotated Teacher Edition. Be sure to give special emphasis to the boldfaced spelling words.
- Create an original oral quiz–or ask a student who has previously demonstrated that he or she has full command of the words in the Word Bank to do so–by using each word from the Word Bank or Spelling Application exercise in a sentence.

Monitor Progress   Students should be encouraged to take responsibility for their own learning and to monitor their progress as they learn new spelling patterns and concepts. Students may monitor their progress in the following ways:

- After completing an exercise, students can check the spelling words against the Word Bank list and circle any misspelled words. They can then review the information presented in Key Concepts and try those items again.
- Students can create and maintain a chart listing exercises and scores.
- Students can keep a log of troublesome words. They can add to the log other vocabulary words that follow the same spelling pattern.

You might ask students to give you periodic reports of their spelling achievement. By keeping track of how students are faring, you can make accommodations in your teaching, accelerating the pace for some and slowing it down for those who need additional support. The following strategies may be used:

- Ask students to complete the lesson exercises in class or as homework; keep track of their scores and of the spelling words that give students the most difficulty. Review relevant spelling concepts with individual students or with small groups.

- Assess only the Spelling Application exercise to see whether students are able to apply what they have learned in the lesson to new spelling words.

- Ask students to complete the Lesson Review, which covers the material in the previous four lessons, to see whether they are remembering the concepts they've learned. Review or reteach as necessary.

Posttest   At the end of a lesson or group of four lessons, conduct a posttest and record the final scores. You might assess student learning in the following ways:

- Administer the Oral Quiz at the end of this Annotated Teacher Edition, giving special emphasis to the boldfaced words.

- Create an original oral quiz by using the words in the Word Bank or in the Spelling Application exercise appropriately in a sentence.

- Use the Lesson Review as a formal posttest for a group of four lessons.

Record Keeping

You may want to photocopy the Student Progress Chart on page vii so that you can maintain a chart for each student in your classroom. Whether you're using a single five-item exercise to monitor progress or an entire Review or Oral Quiz as a final assessment, use the Scoring Scale on pages viii–ix to determine percentage scores. Transfer those scores to students' Progress Charts and then use the charts in conferences with parents and students. You may also wish to track students' scores and spelling achievement using the Theme Progress Charts available in the Theme Planning Guides for *The Reader's Choice* program.

Keep in mind that the Scoring Scale and Student Progress Chart are also available to students in their copies of this *Spelling Power* workbook. Students should be encouraged to use these forms to monitor their own progress as they complete and score lessons and learn the results of any formal assessments you may conduct.

Instructional References

For more about research in spelling instruction, you may want to consult these sources:

Baron, J., R. Treiman, F. Wilf, and P. Kellman. "Spelling and Reading by Rules." *Cognitive Processes in Spelling*. Ed. Uta Frith. London: Academic Press, 1980. 160–194.

Bear, Donald R., Marcia Invernizzi, Shane Templeton, and Francine Johnston. *Words Their Way: Word Study for Phonics, Vocabulary, and Spelling Instruction*. Old Tappan, NJ: Prentice Hall, 1999.

Beers, James. "Developmental Strategies of Spelling Competence in Primary School Children." *Developmental and Cognitive Aspects of Learning to Spell*. Eds. Edmund Henderson and James Beers. Newark, DE: International Reading Association, 1980. 3–21.

Edgar, Dale and Joseph O'Rourke. *The Living Word Vocabulary: A National Vocabulary Inventory*. Chicago: World Book–Childcraft, 1981.

Frith, Uta, ed. *Cognitive Processes in Spelling*. London: Academic Press, 1980.

Fry, Edward Bernard, Jacqueline E. Kress, and Dona Lee Fountoukidis. *The Reading Teacher's Book of Lists*. Paramus, NJ: Prentice-Hall, 1993.

Ganske, Kathy. *Word Journeys: Assessment-Guided Phonics, Spelling, and Vocabulary Instruction*. New York: Guilford, 2000.

Gentry, J. R. "An Analysis of Developmental Spelling in GNYS at WRK." *Reading Teacher* 36 (1982): 192–200.

Henderson, Edmund. "Work Knowledge and Reading Disability." *Developmental and Cognitive Aspects of Learning to Spell*. Eds. Edmund Henderson and James Beers. Newark, DE: International Reading Association, 1980. 161–185.

Moats, Louisa C. "Spelling Error Analysis: Beyond the Phonetic/Dysphonetic Dichotomy." *Annals of Dyslexia* 43 (1993): 174–185.

Rasinski, Timothy V., Nancy D. Padak, Brenda Weible Church, Gay Fawcett, Judith Hendershot, Justina M. Henry, Barbara G. Moss, Jacqueline K. Peck, Elizabeth (Betsy) Pryor, and Kathleen A. Roskos, eds. *Teaching Word Recognition, Spelling, and Vocabulary: Strategies From* The Reading Teacher. Newark, DE: International Reading Association, 2000.

Treiman, Rebecca. *Beginning to Spell*. New York: Cambridge UP, 1993.

Waters, G., M. Bruck, and M. Seidenberg. "Do Children Use Similar Processes to Read and Spell Words?" *Journal of Experimental Child Psychology* 39 (1985): 511–530.

STUDENT PROGRESS CHART

Fill in the chart below with the student's scores, using the scoring scale on the next page.

Name: _____

	Lesson	Pretest	Oral Quiz	Unit Review
1				
2				
3				
4				
Review				
5				
6				
7				
8				
Review				
9				
10				
11				
12				
Review				
13				
14				
15				
16				
Review				
17				
18				
19				
20				
Review				
21				
22				
23				
24				
Review				
25				
26				
27				
28				
Review				
29				
30				
31				
32				
Review				

SCORING SCALE

Use this scale to find a student's score. Line up the number of items with the number correct. For example, if 15 out of 16 items are correct, the score is 93.7 percent (see grayed area).

Number Correct

Number of Items	1	2	3	4	5	6	7	8	9	10	11	12	13	14	15	16	17	18	19	20
1	100																			
2	50	100																		
3	33.3	66.7	100																	
4	25	50	75	100																
5	20	40	60	80	100															
6	16.7	33.3	50	66.7	83.3	100														
7	14.3	28.6	42.9	57.1	71.4	85.7	100													
8	12.5	25	37.5	50	62.5	75	87.5	100												
9	11.1	22.2	33.3	44.4	55.6	66.7	77.8	88.9	100											
10	10	20	30	40	50	60	70	80	90	100										
11	9.1	18.1	27.2	36.3	45.4	54.5	63.6	72.7	81.8	90.9	100									
12	8.3	16.7	25	33.3	41.7	50	58.3	66.7	75	83.3	91.7	100								
13	7.7	15.3	23.1	30.8	38.5	46.1	53.8	61.5	69.2	76.9	84.6	92.3	100							
14	7.1	14.3	21.4	28.6	35.7	42.8	50	57.1	64.3	71.4	78.5	85.7	92.8	100						
15	6.7	13.3	20	26.7	33.3	40	46.6	53.3	60	66.7	73.3	80	86.7	93.3	100					
16	6.3	12.5	18.8	25	31.2	37.5	43.7	50	56.2	62.5	68.7	75	81.2	87.5	93.7	100				
17	5.9	11.8	17.6	23.5	29.4	35.3	41.2	47	52.9	58.8	64.7	70.6	76.5	82.3	88.2	94.1	100			
18	5.6	11.1	16.7	22.2	27.8	33.3	38.9	44.4	50	55.5	61.1	66.7	72.2	77.8	83.3	88.9	94.4	100		
19	5.3	10.5	15.8	21	26.3	31.6	36.8	42.1	47.4	52.6	57.9	63.1	68.4	73.7	78.9	84.2	89.4	94.7	100	
20	5	10	15	20	25	30	35	40	45	50	55	60	65	70	75	80	85	90	95	100
21	4.8	9.5	14.3	19	23.8	28.6	33.3	38.1	42.8	47.6	52.3	57.1	61.9	66.7	71.4	76.1	80.9	85.7	90.5	95.2
22	4.5	9.1	13.7	18.2	22.7	27.3	31.8	36.4	40.9	45.4	50	54.5	59.1	63.6	68.1	72.7	77.2	81.8	86.4	90.9
23	4.3	8.7	13	17.4	21.7	26.1	30.4	34.8	39.1	43.5	47.8	52.1	56.5	60.8	65.2	69.5	73.9	78.3	82.6	86.9
24	4.2	8.3	12.5	16.7	20.8	25	29.2	33.3	37.5	41.7	45.8	50	54.2	58.3	62.5	66.7	70.8	75	79.1	83.3
25	4	8	12	16	20	24	28	32	36	40	44	48	52	56	60	64	68	72	76	80
26	3.8	7.7	11.5	15.4	19.2	23.1	26.9	30.8	34.6	38.5	42.3	46.2	50	53.8	57.7	61.5	65.4	69.2	73.1	76.9
27	3.7	7.4	11.1	14.8	18.5	22.2	25.9	29.6	33.3	37	40.7	44.4	48.1	51.9	55.6	59.2	63	66.7	70.4	74.1
28	3.6	7.1	10.7	14.3	17.9	21.4	25	28.6	32.1	35.7	39.3	42.9	46.4	50	53.6	57.1	60.7	64.3	67.9	71.4
29	3.4	6.9	10.3	13.8	17.2	20.7	24.1	27.6	31	34.5	37.9	41.4	44.8	48.3	51.7	55.2	58.6	62.1	65.5	69
30	3.3	6.7	10	13.3	16.7	20	23.3	26.7	30	33.3	36.7	40	43.3	46.7	50	53.3	56.7	60	63.3	66.7
31	3.2	6.5	9.7	13	16.1	19.3	22.6	25.8	29	32.2	35.4	38.7	41.9	45.1	48.3	51.6	54.8	58	61.2	64.5
32	3.1	6.3	9.4	12.5	15.6	18.8	21.9	25	28.1	31.3	34.4	37.5	40.6	43.8	46.9	50	53.1	56.2	59.4	62.5
33	3	6	9	12.1	15.1	18.1	21.2	24.2	27.2	30.3	33	36.3	39.3	42.4	45.4	48.4	51.5	54.5	57.5	60.6
34	2.9	5.9	8.8	11.8	14.7	17.6	20.6	23.5	26.5	29.4	32.4	35.3	38.2	41.2	44.1	47.1	50	52.9	55.9	58.8
35	2.9	5.7	8.6	11.4	14.3	17.1	20	22.9	25.7	28.6	31.4	34.3	37.1	40	42.9	45.7	48.6	51.4	54.3	57.1
36	2.8	5.6	8.3	11.1	13.9	16.7	19.4	22.2	25	27.8	30.6	33.3	36.1	38.9	41.7	44.4	47.2	50	52.7	55.6
37	2.7	5.4	8.1	10.8	13.5	16.2	18.9	21.6	24.3	27	29.7	32.4	35.1	37.8	40.5	43.2	45.9	48.6	51.4	54
38	2.6	5.3	7.9	10.5	13.2	15.8	18.4	21.1	23.7	26.3	28.9	31.6	34.2	36.8	39.5	42.1	44.7	47.4	50	52.6
39	2.6	5.2	7.7	10.3	12.8	15.4	17.9	20.5	23.1	25.6	28.2	30.8	33.3	35.9	38.5	41	43.6	46.2	48.7	51.3
40	2.5	5	7.5	10	12.5	15	17.5	20	22.5	25	27.5	30	32.5	35	37.5	40	42.5	45	47.5	50

Number Correct

Number of Items	21	22	23	24	25	26	27	28	29	30	31	32	33	34	35	36	37	38	39	40
1																				
2																				
3																				
4																				
5																				
6																				
7																				
8																				
9																				
10																				
11																				
12																				
13																				
14																				
15																				
16																				
17																				
18																				
19																				
20																				
21	100																			
22	95.4	100																		
23	91.3	95.6	100																	
24	87.5	91.6	95.8	100																
25	84	88	92	96	100															
26	80.8	84.6	88.5	92.3	96.2	100														
27	77.8	81.5	85.2	88.9	92.6	96.3	100													
28	75	78.6	82.1	85.7	89.3	92.9	96.4	100												
29	72.4	75.9	79.3	82.8	86.2	89.7	93.1	96.6	100											
30	70	73.3	76.7	80	83.3	86.7	90	93.3	96.7	100										
31	67.7	70.9	74.2	77.4	80.6	83.9	87.1	90.3	93.5	96.8	100									
32	65.6	68.8	71.9	75	78.1	81.2	84.4	87.5	90.6	93.8	96.9	100								
33	63.6	66.7	69.7	72.7	75.8	78.8	81.8	84.8	87.8	90.9	93.9	96.9	100							
34	61.8	64.7	67.6	70.6	73.5	76.5	79.4	82.4	85.3	88.2	91.2	94.1	97.1	100						
35	60	62.9	65.7	68.6	71.4	74.3	77.1	80	82.9	85.7	88.6	91.4	94.3	97.1	100					
36	58.3	61.1	63.8	66.7	69.4	72.2	75	77.8	80.6	83.3	86.1	88.9	91.7	94.4	97.2	100				
37	56.8	59.5	62.2	64.9	67.6	70.3	72.9	75.7	78.4	81.1	83.8	86.5	89.2	91.9	94.6	97.3	100			
38	55.3	57.9	60.5	63.2	65.8	68.4	71.1	73.7	76.3	78.9	81.6	84.2	86.8	89.5	92.1	94.7	97.3	100		
39	53.8	56.4	58.9	61.5	64.1	66.7	69.2	71.8	74.4	76.9	79.5	82.1	84.6	87.2	89.7	92.3	94.9	97.4	100	
40	52.5	55	57.5	60	62.5	65	67.5	70	72.5	75	77.5	80	82.5	85	87.5	90	92.5	95	97.5	100

Spelling Power

Lesson 1: Double Consonants

Word Bank

| accordance | committee | embarrass | exaggerate | omission |
| opposite | parallel | questionnaire | villain | wholly |

Key Concepts

A single consonant sound is sometimes spelled with double consonants. Because the two consonants are not heard individually, learn to visualize these words to spell them correctly.

1. Some common two-syllable words are spelled with double consonants, as in *villain* and *wholly*.
2. Some three-syllable words are spelled with one set of double consonants, as in *accordance, omission, opposite, parallel,* and *questionnaire*.
3. Many longer words of four or more syllables have one set of double consonants, as in *exaggerate*.
4. Some words include more than one set of double consonants, as in *committee* and *embarrass*.

Spelling Practice

Draw a line through the word in each set that is spelled incorrectly. Then write the word correctly on the line provided.

1. ~~ommision~~ parallel
   omission

2. ~~vilain~~ accordance
   villain

3. wholly ~~embarass~~
   embarrass

4. ~~comittee~~ questionnaire
   committee

5. ~~oposite~~ exaggerate
   opposite

6. committee ~~parralel~~
   parallel

7. ~~wholy~~ villain
   wholly

8. opposite ~~questionaire~~
   questionnaire

9. omission ~~acordance~~
   accordance

10. ~~exagerate~~ embarrass
    exaggerate

Spelling in Context

Complete each sentence below with the correct word from the Word Bank.

1. Two lines that are __parallel__ will never intersect.

2. We decided that working as a(n) __committee__ would be more efficient than working individually.

3. "If you mention that you saw her drop her lunch tray, you will definitely __embarrass__ her," said Sadie.

4. Although they are twins, Tom and Todd have completely __opposite__ outlooks on life.

5. The mystery writer is so gifted that you can rarely identify the __villain__ until the last page.

LESSON 1 continued

Proofreading Practice

Read the paragraph below. Find the five misspelled words and circle them. Then write the correct spellings of the words on the lines below the paragraph.

The teacher gave the class instructions before she handed out the (questionaire) She told the students to write their responses in (acordance) with the directions on the survey. She encouraged them to answer all questions, as (ommisions) would make the results useless. She also instructed them not to (exagerate) After she was (wholy) satisfied that the students understood the instructions, the teacher told them to begin.

1. questionnaire   3. omissions   5. wholly

2. accordance   4. exaggerate

Spelling Application

Listed below are ten additional words that fit the patterns you have learned. Read each crossword puzzle clue. Then determine which word matches the clue and write the word in the squares provided.

accommodate	appetite
bulletin	disappoint
hurricane	irrigate
occurrence	opportunity
recommend	sheriff

Across

2. event
3. fail to live up to expectations
6. suggest
7. desire for food
8. officer of the law
10. chance

Down

1. adapt or make suitable
4. to supply with water
5. short official statement
9. storm with violent wind

Spelling Power

Lesson 2: Silent Consonants

Word Bank

autumn	fasten	freight	ghastly	gnaw
knead	limb	pneumonia	psalm	wretched

Key Concepts

Many words in the English language contain consonants that are not sounded. To learn to spell these words, study them and visualize them spelled correctly.

1. In words ending in *mn* or *mb*, the final consonant is silent, as in *autumn* and *limb*.
2. The first letter is silent in words beginning with *kn*, *gn*, *ps*, *pn*, or *wr*, as in *knead*, *gnaw*, *psalm*, *pneumonia*, and *wretched*.
3. The consonant combination *gh* is silent, as in *through* and *freight*.
4. The *h* is silent in words beginning with *gh*, as in *ghastly*.
5. The *t* is often silent when it appears before the letters *en*, as in *fasten*.

Spelling Practice

Listed below are ten spelling patterns. On the line provided, write the word from the Word Bank to which the pattern applies.

1. Silent *w* in the *wr* combination at the beginning of a word — wretched

2. Silent *h* following *g* at the beginning of a word — ghastly

3. Silent *n* in the *mn* combination at the end of a word — autumn

4. Silent *g* before *n* at the beginning of a word — gnaw

5. Silent *t* before *en* — fasten

6. Silent *p* in the *ps* combination at the beginning of a word — psalm

7. Silent *p* in the *pn* combination at the beginning of a word — pneumonia

8. Silent consonant combination *gh* — freight

9. Silent *b* in a word ending with *mb* — limb

10. Silent *k* in a word beginning with *kn* — knead

Name _____ Date _____ Class _____

Spelling in Context

In each sentence below, find the misspelled word and circle it. Then write the word correctly on the line.

1. You should (nead) the dough until it is elastic and no longer sticky.   knead

2. Although the rats (naw) at the cheese in the trap, they never get caught.   gnaw

3. The musician set her favorite (salm) to music so that it could be sung at her wedding.   psalm

4. The (gastly) noises were coming from the engine of the old car.   ghastly

5. The flight attendant asked passengers to (fassen) their seatbelts.   fasten

Proofreading Practice

Read the paragraph below. Find the five misspelled words and circle them. Then write the correct spellings of the words on the lines below the paragraph.

The small boy, who had been hospitalized with (neumonia) watched out his window as the (freit) train rushed by and a sparrow sang on a tree (limm). Although he was in (retched) health when he was admitted to the hospital, he now felt better. He hoped to be home in early (autum).

1. pneumonia   3. limb   5. autumn

2. freight   4. wretched

Spelling Application

Listed below are five additional words that have silent consonants. Find them in the word maze and circle them. Then write the word that fits each pattern on the lines provided.

ghost   knowledge   psychology   through   wrench

1. Silent *k* in a word beginning with *kn*
   knowledge

2. Silent *w* in a word beginning with *wr*
   wrench

3. Silent *p* in a word beginning with *ps*
   psychology

4. Silent consonant combination *gh*
   through

5. Silent *h* in a word beginning with *gh*
   ghost

Spelling Power

Lesson 3: Sounds of c and g

Word Bank

ancestry	censor	circumstance	disguise	genius
gymnasium	plague	recapture	recipe	tragedy

Key Concepts

The letters *c* and *g* may sound soft or hard depending on the vowels or consonants that follow them. A soft *c* sounds like \s\, and a hard *c* sounds like \k\. A soft *g* sounds like \j\, and a hard *g* sounds like \g\. Knowing the following patterns will help you spell words that include the letters *c* and *g*. Visualize how these words look as you become familiar with their spelling.

1. The letter *c* has a soft sound \s\ when it is directly followed by *e, i,* or *y,* as in *ancestry, censor,* and *recipe.* This pattern is also illustrated by the first *c* and the final *c* in *circumstance.*

2. The letter *c* has a hard sound \k\ when it is followed by *a, o, u,* or any consonant, as in *recapture.* This pattern is also illustrated by the second *c* in *circumstance.*

3. The letter *g* is pronounced \j\ when it is followed by *e, i,* or *y,* as in *genius, gymnasium,* and *tragedy.*

4. A *g* has a hard sound \g\ when it is followed by *a, o, u,* or any consonant, as in *disguise* and *plague.*

Spelling Practice

Draw a line through the word in each set that is spelled incorrectly. Then write the word correctly.

1. ~~disgise~~   tragedy
   disguise

2. ~~resipe~~   censor
   recipe

3. genius   ~~cirkumstance~~
   circumstance

4. ~~ansestry~~   gymnasium
   ancestry

5. recapture   ~~plage~~
   plague

6. ~~sensor~~   ancestry
   censor

7. ~~trajedy~~   plague
   tragedy

8. ~~jenius~~   disguise
   genius

9. recipe   ~~jymnasium~~
   gymnasium

10. ~~rekapture~~   circumstance
    recapture

Spelling in Context

Decide which word from the Word Bank is defined in each phrase below. Then write the word on the line.

1. to conceal one's identity
   disguise

2. someone who is extraordinarily intelligent
   genius

3. to remove potentially sensitive or offensive passages or words from a text
   censor

LESSON 3 continued

4. a place where athletic activity is performed   _gymnasium_

5. a list of ingredients and the procedure for their preparation   _recipe_

Proofreading Practice

Read the paragraph below. Find the five misspelled words and circle them. Then write the correct spellings of the words on the lines below the paragraph.

Countless Europeans experienced great (trajedy) when the (plage) swept the continent in the Middle Ages. They had no idea of the (cirkumstance) that led to the spread of the disease. As the epidemic became widespread in the cities, persons of noble (ansestry) often fled to their country estates in an attempt to escape the sickness and to (rekapture) some sense of normalcy in their lives.

1. tragedy   **4.** ancestry

2. plague   **5.** recapture

3. circumstance

Spelling Application

Listed below are ten additional words that fit the patterns you have learned. Read each crossword puzzle clue. Then determine which word matches the clue and write the word in the squares provided.

bicycle   calculate   extravagance   fragile   gradual

imaginary   necessary   science   success   vegetables

Across

2. favorable outcome
4. carrots, peas, corn
5. required
8. not real
9. to compute
10. delicate; easily broken

Down

1. organized knowledge
3. luxury
6. little by little
7. two-wheeled vehicle with pedals

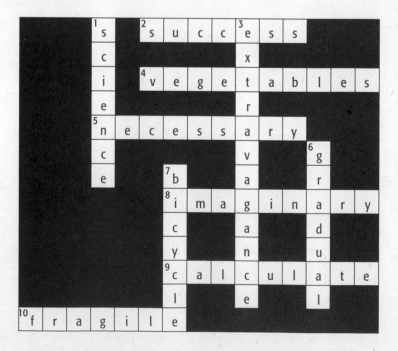

Spelling Power

Lesson 4: Vowel Spellings

Word Bank

acquaintance	bureau	chieftain	gauge	guidepost
haughty	nuisance	peasant	rouse	thorough

Key Concepts

Many words have vowel pairs or combinations that do not follow regular patterns of pronunciation. To learn to spell these words, study them and visualize them spelled correctly.

1. The vowel pair *ou* can be pronounced as the long *o* sound (\ō\), as in *thorough*, or as the vowel sound (\o͞o\), as in *rouse*.

2. The vowel pair *ai* can be pronounced as a long *a* (\ā\), as in *acquaintance*, or as an \ə\ sound, as in *chieftain*.

3. The vowel pair *ui* can be pronounced as a long *i* (\ī\), as in *guidepost*, or as a long *u* (\ū\), as in *nuisance*.

4. The vowel pair *au* can be pronounced as an \ô\ sound, as in *haughty*, or as a long *a* (\ā\), as in *gauge*.

5. The vowel pair *ea* has several sounds including a long *e* (\ē\), as in *heathen*, and a short *e* (\e\) as in *peasant*.

6. The combination *cau* at the end of words creates the long *o* (\ō\) sound, as in *bureau*.

Spelling Practice

Draw a line through the word in each set that is spelled incorrectly. Then write the word correctly.

1. ~~thoro~~   peasant
   thorough _____

2. ~~gydepost~~   privilege
   guidepost _____

3. acquaintance   ~~buro~~
   bureau _____

4. haughty   ~~gage~~
   gauge _____

5. ~~newsance~~   thorough
   nuisance _____

6. ~~chieftan~~   bureau
   chieftain _____

7. ~~ruse~~   nuisance
   rouse _____

8. ~~hawghty~~   chieftain
   haughty _____

9. ~~pesant~~   guidepost
   peasant _____

10. gauge   ~~acquayntance~~
    acquaintance _____

Spelling in Context

Complete each sentence with the correct word from the Word Bank.

1. He could not __gauge_____ whether his van would fit under the bridge.

2. The __bureau_____ was crammed with children's toys and books.

3. When the janitorial staff completed their __thorough_____ cleaning, the floors shone.

LESSON 4 continued

4. A lighthouse serves as a _____guidepost_____ for mariners navigating coastal waters.

5. Meera was surprised when her _____acquaintance_____ from the workshop greeted her like an old friend.

Proofreading Practice

Read the paragraph below. Find the five misspelled words and circle them. Then write the correct spellings of the words on the lines below the paragraph.

Pascal drifted into a daydream as he read his history assignment. In his dream, he was a (chieftan) in ancient England. He ruled his people with a firm but fair hand and treated even the lowliest (pesant) with respect. His attitude was never (hawghty.) Every subject was either a friend or acquaintance. No one was considered a (newsance.) Just then his book slipped off the desk, serving to (rooz) him.

1. chieftain   4. nuisance

2. peasant   5. rouse

3. haughty

Spelling Application

Listed below are five additional words that fit the patterns you have learned. Find these words in the word maze and circle them. Then write the words on the lines provided.

boundary   captain   heathen   plateau   taut

```
i  p  e  r  t  z  h  p  l  a  t  e  a  u  y  y
v  a  d  g  q  u  o  t  w  m  j  f  e  y  r
h  e  y  u  i  l  c  d  w  s  t  p  k  v  a
o  e  v  c  b  t  a  u  t  h  l  y  y  m  d
t  p  a  x  s  d  l  t  e  q  s  o  p  h  n
u  v  a  t  c  d  a  h  l  y  h  b  c  k  u
r  o  a  g  h  l  t  p  a  m  s  t  i  m  o
a  b  s  l  t  e  e  t  i  y  o  m  s  r  b
h  e  n  m  e  g  n  c  a  p  t  a  i  n  z
```

1. plateau   4. taut

2. boundary   5. captain

3. heathen

Spelling Power

Unit 1 Review

Lessons 1–4
Draw a line through the word in each set that is spelled incorrectly. Then write the word correctly.

1. exaggerate

   ~~disgise~~

   disguise

2. ~~villan~~

   plague

   villain

3. ~~salm~~

   bureau

   psalm

4. chieftain

   ~~trajedy~~

   tragedy

5. gnaw

   ~~retched~~

   wretched

6. ~~buro~~

   tragedy

   bureau

7. ~~naw~~

   disguise

   gnaw

8. ~~plage~~

   wretched

   plague

9. ~~chieftan~~

   psalm

   chieftain

10. villain

    ~~exagerate~~

    exaggerate

In each of the following sentences, find the misspelled word and circle it. Then write the word's correct spelling on the line provided.

11. Descended from a long line of missionaries, the boy was proud of his (ansestry.) ancestry

12. The doctor warned her against strenuous activity after her battle with (neumonia.) pneumonia

13. The (gidepost) knocked over in the storm, was no help to lost tourists. guidepost

14. The (ommission) of test directions caused confusion. omission

15. Place the rows (paralel) to each other, not at right angles. parallel

16. The (hawghty) doorman turned us away from the hotel even though we had reservations. haughty

17. The producer decided to (sensor) the film before it was aired on television. censor

18. The third model in the fashion show wore a (pesant) dress. peasant

19. My hands became tired after several minutes of trying to (nead) the dense dough. knead

20. Some people always (embarass) others with their tactless comments. embarrass

Spelling Power

Proofreading Application

Lessons 1–4
Read the following article from a student newspaper. Find twenty misspelled words and circle them. Then write the correct spelling for each word on the lines below the article.

Harvest Dance a Great Success

On October 12, at 8:00 P.M., the first Fall Festival was held in the magically transformed school gymnasium. Originally, the activity committee had scheduled the dance for January. However, the members decided that an autum dance would give students a chance to make the acquantance of others who were not in their classes. The comittee felt that this occasion would get the school year off to a good start.

By October 11, almost all of the students had purchased tickets to the dance. In acordance with school regulations, students had to submit permission slips from their parents and sign pledges that they would abide wholy by the rules for the function. When asked whether students believed that these precautions were excessive, Minerva Ty, a sophomore, replied, "I think most feel as I do. It is a privilege to go to a school that cares enough to provide events like this for us. Let's not exagerate problems."

Meanwhile, the students in charge of decorating were busy behind the scenes. They planned ahead so that anything to be delivered by freit truck would arrive in time. Initially, the students thought about having a haunted house theme with gastly sound effects and scary decorations. However, a party genius came up with the oposite idea of a fall festival. Students brought in or made small trees and decided to fasen streamers in fall colors to each lim. Volunteers cut out hundreds of bright leaves to suspend from the ceiling and place in piles around the edge of the room. They then had to gage how much room they should leave for the dance floor and where small tables could be placed. Bowls of polished apples and party favors on each table completed the decor. In keeping with the theme, the refreshments included cider and doughnuts. Senior Jason Belloma remarked, "The party planners wrote a resipe for success."

All who attended the dance complimented the event. The only newsance was that the time went too quickly. The chaperones were impressed by the thoro organization of the activity. Principal Pace said, "The event helped us rekapture some of the school spirit that had been lagging. It was a positive sircumstance in every way." On the follow-up questionaire students raved about the dance. One student wrote, "Let's make the Fall Festival a tradition!"

1.	gymnasium	8.	freight	15.	recipe
2.	autumn	9.	ghastly	16.	nuisance
3	acquaintance	10.	genius	17.	thorough
4.	committee	11.	opposite	18.	recapture
5.	accordance	12.	fasten	19.	circumstance
6.	wholly	13.	limb	20.	questionnaire
7.	exaggerate	14.	gauge		

Spelling Power

Lesson 5: Diphthongs and Vowel + *r* Shifts

Word Bank

aerial	aisle	authentic	guardian	rehearsal
souvenir	soybean	trapezoid	undoubtedly	uproarious

Key Concepts

When two vowels are combined, their individual sounds become blended into a single sound called a diphthong. A vowel sound also changes or shifts when the vowel is followed by the letter *r*. Keep the following guidelines in mind when spelling words that have blended vowel sounds or shifted vowel sounds.

1. The sound \ā\ may be spelled *ae*, as in *aerial*.
2. The sound \ô\ may be spelled *aw*, as in *thaw*, or *au*, as in *authentic*.
3. The sound \ī\ may be spelled *ai*, as in *aisle*, or *ay*, as in *bayou*.
4. The sound \oi\ may be spelled *oy*, as in *soybean*, or *oi*, as in *trapezoid*.
5. The sound \o͞o\ may be spelled *oo*, as in *moon*, or *ou*, as in *souvenir*.
6. The sound \ou\ may be spelled *ow*, as in *empower*, or *ou*, as in *undoubtedly*.
7. The sound \är\ may be spelled *ar*, as in *start*, or *uar*, as in *guardian*.
8. The sound \ur\ may be spelled *er*, as in *clerk*; *ir*, as in *dirt*; *ur*, as in *turn*; or *ear*, as in *rehearsal*.
9. The sound \ôr\ may be spelled *or*, as in *store*, or *oar*, as in *uproarious*.

Spelling Practice

Draw a line through the word in each set that is spelled incorrectly. Then write the word correctly on the line provided.

1. souvenir ~~awthentic~~ — authentic
2. ~~undowbtedly~~ aisle — undoubtedly
3. ~~arial~~ trapezoid — aerial
4. rehearsal ~~ile~~ — aisle
5. authentic ~~rehursal~~ — rehearsal
6. ~~gardian~~ aerial — guardian
7. ~~soibean~~ undoubtedly — soybean
8. uproarious ~~soovenir~~ — souvenir
9. ~~uprorious~~ guardian — uproarious
10. ~~trapezoyd~~ soybean — trapezoid

LESSON 5 continued

Spelling in Context

In each sentence below, find the misspelled word and circle it. Then write its correct spelling on the line.

1. He bought a (soovenir) to remind him of his visit to New Hampshire.   souvenir

2. Matt's performance in the talent competition was (uprorious)   uproarious

3. Farmers are hoping the hot, dry weather will not ruin their (soibean) crops.   soybean

4. The (airial) photographs of the Grand Canyon were spectacular.   aerial

5. He won an award for designing a building in the shape of a (trapezoyd).   trapezoid

Proofreading Practice

Read the paragraph below. Find the five misspelled words and circle them. Then write the correct spellings of the words on the lines below the paragraph.

The wedding (rehirsal) did not go as smoothly as planned. As the bride walked down the (aysle) on the arm of her (gardian) she tripped over the train of her (awthentic) Victorian gown. Then the minister mispronounced her name. She was worried until she realized that everything that could go wrong already had. The wedding the next day would (undowtedly) go well.

1. rehearsal   3. guardian   5. undoubtedly

2. aisle   4. authentic

Spelling Application

Listed below are ten words that fit the patterns you have learned. Read each scrambled word. Then write the words correctly on the lines provided.

clerk	devout	empower	outbound	point
royalty	start	store	turmoil	turnpike

1. seotr   store   6. yoarylt   royalty

2. reklc   clerk   7. tuedov   devout

3. inopt   point   8. muiltor   turmoil

4. wpomree   empower   9. buutoodn   outbound

5. tstar   start   10. kentruip   turnpike

Spelling Power

Lesson 6: Use of *ie* and *ei*

Word Bank

achieve	ceiling	counterfeit	deceive	either
grieve	niece	vein	weigh	weird

Key Concepts

Many people commit the following rhyme to memory so that they will know whether to use *ie* or *ei* in the spelling of a word:

Put *i* before *e* except after *c* or when sounded like \ā\, as in *neighbor* and *weigh*.

Remembering the following additional guidelines will help even more. Visualize the exceptions to the rule as you study them.

1. Use the *ie* spelling when the letter *c* or *t* appears before *i* to signal the \sh\ sound, as in *conscience*.

2. Commit these exceptions to memory: *counterfeit, ceiling, either,* and *weird.*

Spelling Practice

Draw a line through the word in each set that is spelled incorrectly. Then write the word correctly on the line provided.

1. ~~counterfiet~~
   niece
   counterfeit

2. ~~greive~~
   either
   grieve

3. ~~wierd~~
   weigh
   weird

4. ceiling
   ~~neice~~
   niece

5. ~~decieve~~
   weird
   deceive

6. ~~vien~~
   counterfeit
   vein

7. deceive
   ~~iether~~
   either

8. ~~acheive~~
   grieve
   achieve

9. vein
   ~~wiegh~~
   weigh

10. achieve
    ~~cieling~~
    ceiling

LESSON 6 continued

Spelling in Context

Complete each sentence below with the correct word from the Word Bank.

1. I sent my __niece__ a gift for her birthday.

2. The dream I had last night was very __weird__.

3. The cashier found a __counterfeit__ $20 bill in the cash register.

4. He wanted to be left alone to __grieve__ for the loss of his dog.

5. The butcher will __weigh__ the meat on the scale.

Proofreading Practice

Read the paragraph below. Find the five misspelled words and circle them. Then write the correct spellings of the words on the lines below the paragraph.

Zack sat in the auditorium and stared at the (cieling) trying to calm down, but it was difficult. He could still feel the (vien) in his neck pulsing. He knew that Eric hadn't intentionally tried to (decieve) him when he told Zack the wrong time for the audition. By the time Zack discovered Eric's mistake and ran to the auditorium, all the leading roles had been cast. Now Zack would not be able to (acheive) his goal of starring in the school play. He would have to be satisfied with being a member of (iether) the chorus or the stage crew.

1. __ceiling__   3. __deceive__   5. __either__

2. __vein__   4. __achieve__

Spelling Application

Listed below are five additional words that fit the patterns you have learned. Read each scrambled word. Then write the words correctly on the lines provided.

conscience   forfeit   pier   receive   yield

1. riep   __pier__

2. ecvreei   __receive__

3. seecnccoin   __conscience__

4. tiffero   __forfeit__

5. yelid   __yield__

Spelling Power

Lesson 7: Doubling the Final Consonant

Word Bank

admittance	begged	conference	controlling	governing
meanness	permitted	redden	totally	visited

Key Concepts

When certain suffixes are added to word roots that end in a consonant, the final consonant may or may not be doubled. If the final consonant is preceded by another consonant, it is not doubled, as in *governing*. When the final consonant is preceded by a vowel, use the following guidelines to determine whether to double the consonant.

1. Double the final consonant of a one-syllable word if the suffix begins with a vowel, as in *begged* and *redden*.

2. Double the final consonant if the stress is placed on the last syllable of the word root, as in *admittance, controlling*, and *permitted*.

3. Do not double the final consonant if the suffix begins with a vowel and the last syllable of the word root is not stressed, as in *visited*.

4. Do not double the final consonant if the suffix begins with a vowel and the last syllable of the word root is not stressed after the suffix is added, as in *conference*.

5. Do not double the final consonant if the suffix begins with a consonant, such as *-ly* or *-ness,* as in *totally* and *meanness*.

Spelling Practice

Combine each word and suffix and write the new word on the line provided.

1. admit + ance = ___admittance___
2. beg + ed = ___begged___
3. confer + ence = ___conference___
4. control + ing = ___controlling___
5. govern + ing = ___governing___

6. mean + ness = ___meanness___
7. permit + ed = ___permitted___
8. red + en = ___redden___
9. total + ly = ___totally___
10. visit + ed = ___visited___

Spelling in Context

In each sentence below, find the misspelled word and circle it. Then write the correct spelling of the word on the line provided.

1. The child (beged) her mother for another new toy. ___begged___

2. We hoped the bully would learn to control his (meaness). ___meanness___

3. The sky began to (reden) as the sun set. ___redden___

4. He enjoyed (controling) the electric train. ___controlling___

5. We needed extra tickets to gain (admitance) to the show. ___admittance___

Name _____ Date _____ Class _____

Proofreading Practice

Read the paragraph below. Find the five misspelled words and circle them. Then write the correct spellings of the words on the lines below the paragraph.

When our class visitted the aluminum factory, we were totaly surprised by the size of building. The plant manager spoke to us in a large conferrence room and then showed us how the company recycles aluminum products. For safety reasons, we were not permited to touch the machinery. The manager pointed out a sign that listed all the safety rules governning the operation of the equipment.

1. visited

2. totally

3. conference

4. permitted

5. governing

Spelling Application

Listed below are five additional words that fit the patterns you have learned. Find them in the word maze and circle them. Then write the word or words from the maze to which each pattern applies on the lines provided.

accidentally   beginning   occasionally   referred   transferred

```
h  j  f  w  e  r  b  d  n  t  e  k
g  n  i  n  n  i  g  e  b  e  a  c
m  d  n  o  f  c  m  r  i  a  t  f
h  o  y  r  t  o  j  r  l  l  y  j
p  a  u  d  r  e  f  e  r  r  e  d
r  s  i  l  l  a  p  f  r  b  t  m
y  l  l  a  n  o  i  s  a  c  c  o
e  u  a  d  j  h  r  n  t  g  a  o
e  n  i  o  g  i  m  a  c  n  s  l
l  m  a  e  s  s  f  r  r  i  g  e
a  c  c  i  d  e  n  t  a  l  l  y
```

1. Pattern 1: The suffix begins with a consonant. accidentally   occasionally

2. Pattern 2: The suffix begins with a vowel and is added to a word whose last syllable is accented and ends in a vowel and a single consonant.

   beginning   referred   transferred

Spelling Power

Lesson 8: The Final Silent e

Word Bank

acknowledgment	advantageous	enforcement	guaranteeing	manageable
noticeable	scarcity	shoeing	truly	virtuous

Key Concepts

When a suffix is added to a word ending in silent *e*, the *e* may be kept or dropped. The following guidelines can be used to determine the correct spelling. Visualize these words as you study them.

1. Keep the *e* when the suffix begins with a consonant, as in *enforcement.*

2. In most cases, drop the *e* when the suffix begins with a vowel, as in *scarcity* and *virtuous.*

3. However, keep the *e* when the word ends in *ce* or *ge* and the suffix begins with *a* or *o,* as in *advantageous, manageable,* and *noticeable.*

4. Keep the *e* when the word ends in *ee* or *oe* and the suffix begins with a vowel, as in *guaranteeing* and *shoeing.*

5. Some words are exceptions to these patterns and must be committed to memory. Examples are *acknowledgment* and *truly.*

Spelling Practice

Combine each word and suffix and write the new word on the line provided.

1. guarantee + ing = _guaranteeing_

2. advantage + ous = _advantageous_

3. scarce + ity = _scarcity_

4. true + ly = _truly_

5. acknowledge + ment = _acknowledgment_

6. shoe + ing = _shoeing_

7. manage + able = _manageable_

8. enforce + ment = _enforcement_

9. virtue + ous = _virtuous_

10. notice + able = _noticeable_

Spelling in Context

Decide which word from the Word Bank is defined in each phrase below. Then write the word on the line provided.

1. covering an object to protect it from wear   _shoeing_

2. something given to recognize an act or achievement   _acknowledgment_

3. morally pure and good   _virtuous_

4. ensuring that people uphold the laws   _enforcement_

5. an inadequate supply   _scarcity_

LESSON 8 continued

Proofreading Practice

Read the paragraph below. Find the five misspelled words and circle them. Then write the correct spellings of the words on the lines below the paragraph.

Maria (truely) needs to find a new building for her antique shop. Cramming so many pieces of furniture into such a small store is no longer (managable.) There is not enough room to walk through the store without knocking over something. She would like to rent a building with a large storefront so that her window displays would be very (noticable.) Maria is hoping to find an (advantagous) location close to the busiest stores downtown, (guaranteing) heavy customer traffic.

1. truly
2. manageable
3. noticeable
4. advantageous
5. guaranteeing

Spelling Application

Listed below are ten additional words that fit patterns you have learned. Read each crossword puzzle clue. Then determine which word matches the clue and write the word in the squares provided.

agreeing   arrangement   changeable   closing   courageous
density   judgment   lying   sincerely   surely

Across
4. with certainty
5. not telling the truth
6. conclusion
7. an orderly placement
9. genuinely
10. a decision reached

Down
1. likely to vary
2. brave
3. thickness
8. having the same opinion

Spelling Power

Unit 2 Review

Lessons 5–8
Draw a line through the word in each set that is spelled incorrectly. Then write the word correctly on the line provided.

1. aisle

   ~~gardian~~

   guardian _____

2. ~~greive~~

   deceive

   grieve _____

3. ~~visitted~~

   permitted

   visited _____

4. virtuous

   ~~managable~~

   manageable _____

5. ~~trapezoyd~~

   aerial

   trapezoid _____

Add the suffix indicated to each word and write the word on the line provided.

6. mean + ness =

   meanness _____

7. red + en =

   redden _____

8. shoe + ing =

   shoeing _____

9. true + ly =

   truly _____

10. beg + ed =

    begged _____

In each sentence below, find the misspelled word and circle it. Then write the correct spelling of the word on the line provided.

11. The historian thought the papers might be (counterfit) but they were authentic.   counterfeit _____

12. My (neice) sent me an invitation to her high school graduation.   niece _____

13. The shipping company gained many customers by (guaranteing) overnight delivery.   guaranteeing _____

14. People came from all over the world to hear him speak at the (conferrence).   conference _____

15. We should (waigh) the evidence carefully before passing judgment.   weigh _____

16. The prospector located a (vien) of gold between the layers of rock.   vein _____

17. The antics of the actor in the comedy were (uprorious).   uproarious _____

18. Sam was relieved to see that the dent on the car door was barely (noticable).   noticeable _____

19. No one is (permited) in the pool when the lifeguard is not on duty.   permitted _____

20. The dress (rehursal) for the play is scheduled for Thursday night.   rehearsal _____

Spelling Power

Proofreading Application

Lessons 5–8
Read the newspaper article below. Find the twenty misspelled words and circle them. Then write the correct spellings of the words on the lines below the article.

Company Accused of Deceiving State Inspectors, Customers

Officials at AgraProd are denying reports today that they are deliberately trying to decieve iether the state inspectors or the general public in an attempt to acheive a more advantagous position in the marketplace. Inspectors found noticable stockpiles of straw and cottonseed at three of AgraProd's processing plants. There was also evidence of extensive rot in the company's silos.

AgraProd has long been involved in research in the use of corn and soibeans to make common household products such as crayons, wallboard, and cieling tiles. In recent years, however, an upstart company, BestAgra, has been controling that market by offering awthentic soovenir containers and using television ads featuring wierd but lovable furry green creatures.

"AgraProd is undowbtedly causing the scarceity in crops and other raw materials," said BestAgra president, Roy Pickett. "Moreover, they are using inferior materials in their products in an attempt to undersell us."

Law enforcment officials have confirmed that AgraProd may have violated laws governning the harvesting and storage of organic crops. If the charges prove to be true, AgraProd will face stiff fines. AgraProd has scheduled a press conferrence for tomorrow to discuss the state's findings.

Meanwhile, AgraProd's president, Lester Deaton, insists that his company did nothing wrong. In his acknowledgement of the charges against AgraProd, he said, "At the press conference, which will allow admitance to a limited number of journalists, there will not be any admission of wrongdoing. The company will totaly stand behind all of its fine products, guaranteing their quality."

1. deceive
2. either
3. achieve
4. advantageous
5. noticeable
6. soybeans
7. ceiling
8. controlling
9. authentic
10. souvenir

11. weird
12. undoubtedly
13. scarcity
14. enforcement
15. governing
16. conference
17. acknowledgment
18. admittance
19. totally
20. guaranteeing

Spelling Power

Lesson 9: Words Ending in *y*

Word Bank

betrayal	controversial	defiance	envious	implies
laid	overjoyed	readiness	steadily	verifying

Key Concepts

A suffix is an ending added to a word that changes the form of the word. Adding a suffix to a word that ends in *y* may require a change in the word's spelling. The following guidelines will help you decide whether the spelling should be changed and, if so, how to change it. Try to visualize the spellings of these words to help you remember them.

1. If the word has a consonant before the final *y,* change the *y* to *i.*

   controversy + al = controversial   envy + ous = envious   ready + ness = readiness

   defy + ance = defiance   imply + es = implies   steady + ly = steadily

2. If there is a vowel before the final *y,* do not change the *y.*   4. If the suffix is -*ing,* do not change the *y.*

   betray + al = betrayal   verify + ing = verifying

   overjoy + ed = overjoyed

3. If the word is a one-syllable word, do not change the *y.*   5. Remember that there will be exceptions to these patterns.

   shy + ness = shyness   lay + ed = laid

Spelling Practice

Combine each word and suffix and write the new word on the line provided.

1. verify + ing = _verifying_
2. defy + ance = _defiance_
3. lay + ed = _laid_
4. betray + al = _betrayal_
5. controversy + al = _controversial_

6. ready + ness = _readiness_
7. imply + es = _implies_
8. overjoy + ed = _overjoyed_
9. envy + ous = _envious_
10. steady + ly = _steadily_

Spelling in Context

In each sentence, find the misspelled word and circle it. Then write the word correctly.

1. Lucy's hunched posture (implyes) that she is unhappy.   _implies_
2. The goose (layed) a golden egg.   _laid_
3. Eric was (overjoied) to see her.   _overjoyed_
4. I am having difficulty (verifing) the flight arrangements.   _verifying_
5. The book addressed a (controversyal) topic.   _controversial_

Name _____ Date _____ Class _____

LESSON 9 continued

Proofreading Practice

Read the paragraph below. Find the five misspelled words and circle them. Then write the correct spellings of the words on the lines below the paragraph.

Candace could not think straight. All she could focus on was her friend's betraial How could Marti do this to her? Her readyness to tell Doug that Candace liked him showed that Marti had absolutely no regard for her feelings. She was probably just envyous because she liked Doug herself, Candace thought in defyance. That made her feel a little better. Candace took a deep breath and reached for her notebook. She steadyly ripped out the letter she had written to Doug and tore it to pieces.

1. betrayal

2. readiness

3. envious

4. defiance

5. steadily

Spelling Application

Listed below are five additional words that fit the patterns you have learned. Find them in the word maze and circle them. Then write the word or words from the maze to which each pattern applies on the lines provided.

employer   manliness   merciful   shinnied   unifying

```
u n i f y i n g m a
h e e m p l o y e r
i a l a f n a o r b
s h i n n i e d c n
j g c l i m q p i a
e n d i n g t o f r
k d i n g a s r u t
t o y e i r c a l i
f e a s r t l x u w
o r t s q e z o y v
```

1. Pattern 1: If the original word has a consonant before the *y*, change the *y* to *i*.

   manliness   merciful   shinnied

2. Pattern 2: If the original word has a vowel before the *y*, do not change the *y*.

   employer

3. Pattern 3: If the suffix is *-ing*, do not change the *y*.

   unifying

Spelling Power

Lesson 10: Plurals for Nouns Ending in Consonants

Word Bank

approaches	cuffs	fezes	guesses	handkerchiefs
indexes	loaves	scarves	splashes	wolves

Key Concepts

Changing most words from singular to plural form alters their spelling. Usually the plural of a noun is formed by adding *s* to the singular form. However, when a noun ends in certain consonants, the plural is formed differently. Use the following guidelines to remember how to form the plural of these exceptions. Visualize the spelling of these words as you study them.

1. Add *es* to a noun that ends in *ch, z, s, x,* or *sh,* as in *approaches, fezes, guesses, indexes,* and *splashes.*

2. Sometimes when a noun ends in *f,* change the *f* to a *v* and add *es,* so that *loaf* becomes *loaves, scarf* becomes *scarves,* and *wolf* becomes *wolves.*

3. For other nouns ending in *f,* keep the final *f* and add *s,* as in *beliefs* and *handkerchiefs.*

Spelling Practice

Draw a line through the word in each set that is spelled incorrectly. Then write the word correctly.

1. ~~loafs~~   loaves
   loaves

2. indexes   ~~index~~
   indexes

3. handkerchiefs   ~~handkerchieves~~
   handkerchiefs

4. ~~fezs~~   fezes
   fezes, fezzes

5. ~~splashs~~   splashes
   splashes

6. wolves   ~~wolfs~~
   wolves

7. ~~cufves~~   cuffs
   cuffs

8. guesses   ~~guesss~~
   guesses

9. scarves   ~~scarfs~~
   scarves

10. ~~approachs~~   approaches
    approaches

Spelling in Context

Complete each sentence with the correct word from the Word Bank.

1. Upon entering the bakery, Karen smelled the freshly baked _loaves_ of bread.

2. The men wore red felt _fezes_ for the ceremony.

3. The campers were afraid there might be _wolves_ lurking in the woods.

4. Stacy's sister gave her three _guesses_ as to what the present might be.

5. A few _splashes_ of lemon juice always make a salad tasty.

LESSON 10 continued

Proofreading Practice

Read the paragraph below. Find the five misspelled words and circle them. Then write the correct spellings of the words on the lines below the paragraph.

Sara neatly folded the (handkerchieves) and (scarfs) on the display case. Satisfied with the results, she turned to adjust the (cuffes) on the shirt nearby. Then she checked the (indexs) of inventory. Finally everything was ready for the grand opening. She anxiously awaited the customers' (approachs).

1. handkerchiefs

2. scarves

3. cuffs

4. indexes

5. approaches

Spelling Application

Listed below are ten additional words that fit the patterns you have learned. Read each crossword puzzle clue. Then determine which word matches the clue and write the word in the squares provided.

| beliefs | buses | chiefs | dishes | flashes |
| knives | peaches | shelves | wishes | wives |

Across
3. plural of flash
4. plural of peach
5. plural of wife
6. plural of bus
8. plural of dish

Down
1. plural of chief
2. plural of shelf
5. plural of wish
6. plural of belief
7. plural of knife

Spelling Power

Lesson 11: Plurals for Nouns Ending in Vowels

Word Bank

agencies	buys	categories	heroes	memos
pianos	radios	skis	tacos	tattoos

Key Concepts

Forming the plural of a noun that ends in a vowel sometimes presents a spelling challenge. The particular spelling that is used to form its plural depends upon the noun's final vowel and the letter that precedes it. Follow these guidelines when forming the plural of a noun that ends in a vowel. Because there are many exceptions to the patterns, try to visualize these words as you study them.

1. Usually, when a noun ends in a vowel + *o*, add *s*, so that *radio* becomes *radios* and *tattoo* becomes *tattoos*.

2. When a noun ends in a consonant + *o*, *s* or *es* may be added; *memo* becomes *memos*, *piano* becomes *pianos*, *taco* becomes *tacos*, but *hero* becomes *heroes*.

3. When a noun ends in a consonant + *y*, replace the *y* with *i* and add *es*, so that *agency* becomes *agencies* and *category* becomes *categories*.

4. When a noun ends in a vowel + *y*, keep the *y* and add *s*, so that *buy* becomes *buys*.

5. When a noun ends in *i*, simply add *s*, so that *ski* becomes *skis*.

Spelling Practice

Decide which ending (*s* or *es*) should be added to create the plural of each word. Then write the new word.

1. agency   agencies
2. piano   pianos
3. buy   buys
4. radio   radios
5. category   categories

6. ski   skis
7. hero   heroes
8. taco   tacos
9. memo   memos
10. tattoo   tattoos

Spelling in Context

Use context clues to determine which word from the Word Bank fits in each blank. Then write the word on the line.

It didn't take Ryan long to devour two (1) __tacos__ with hot sauce at the ball game. In the row ahead, two men were listening to another game on their (2) __radios__. Both men had (3) __tattoos__ decorating their forearms. They jumped up and screamed whenever one of their (4) __heroes__ came up to the plate. What a contrast! Just yesterday Ryan had been on (5) __skis__, racing down the mountain, half a world away.

LESSON 11 continued

Proofreading Practice

Read the paragraph below. Find the five misspelled words and circle them. Then write the correct spellings of the words on the lines below the paragraph.

MEMO TO EMPLOYEES

As of July 1, the following changes will go into effect.

- All (memoes) will be dated with the year written as four digits.
- The (categorys) of products sold will be noted on all bills. (Pianoes) should be listed as a category separate from other musical instruments.
- The list of "best (buyes)" for each month will be displayed in the lobby at all (agencys)

Contact Kathy at extension 2053 if you have any questions.

1. memos   4. buys

2. categories   5. agencies

3. Pianos

Spelling Application

Below are ten additional words that fit the patterns you have learned. Below the list are scrambled forms of the words. Unscramble each word and write it correctly on the line provided.

banjos	companies	displays	echoes	flies
patios	potatoes	silos	tomatoes	videos

1. ocpnimaes   companies

2. eeosch   echoes

3. oaeottms   tomatoes

4. syalpsid   displays

5. soapti   patios

6. osabnj   banjos

7. viosed   videos

8. ifels   flies

9. oestapot   potatoes

10. lossi   silos

Spelling Power

Lesson 12: Plurals with Unusual Forms

Word Bank

alumni	athletics	campuses	children	crises
data	minimums	oxen	series	salmon

Key Concepts

Usually the plural of a noun is formed by adding s or es to its singular form. There are some nouns to which this pattern does not apply. The following guidelines can be helpful in these cases. Try to visualize these unusual words as you study them.

1. A number of nouns use the same form for the singular and the plural. Examples include *athletics, salmon,* and *series.*

2. Some nouns ending in *us* are borrowed from Latin and use the Latin plural in which the *us* is replaced by *i.* For example, *alumnus* becomes *alumni.* For other nouns ending in *us,* the plural is formed by adding *es.* For example, *campus* becomes *campuses.*

3. Some words ending in *um* are borrowed from Latin and use the Latin plural in which the *um* is replaced by *a.* For example, *datum* becomes *data.* For other words ending in *um,* the plural is formed by adding *s.* For example, *minimum* becomes *minimums.*

4. Some English words have irregular plurals. For example, *child* becomes *children* and *ox* becomes *oxen.*

5. For some words ending in *is,* the plural is formed by changing the *i* to *e.* For example, *crisis* becomes *crises.*

Spelling Practice

Listed below are seven spelling patterns. On the lines below each pattern, write the word or words from the Word Bank to which the pattern applies.

1. Pattern 1: singular and plural forms are the same

   athletics

   salmon

   series

2. Pattern 2: *is* changes to *es*

   crises

3. Pattern 3: *es* is added to words ending in *us*

   campuses

4. Pattern 4: *s* is added to words ending in *um*

   minimums

5. Pattern 5: irregular plurals

   oxen

   children

6. Pattern 6: *us* changes to *i*

   alumni

7. Pattern 7: *um* changes to *a*

   data

LESSON 12 continued

Spelling in Context

Decide which word from the Word Bank is described in each sentence. Then write the word on the line provided.

1. This is a large body of information that a scientist might gather. _____ data _____

2. These huge beasts are used in farming. _____ oxen _____

3. A school's sports program might be called by this name. _____ athletics _____

4. These men all graduated from the same school. _____ alumni _____

5. These large fish are a bright orange-pink in color. _____ salmon _____

Proofreading Practice

Read the paragraph below. Find the five misspelled words and circle them. Then write the correct spellings of the words on the lines below the paragraph.

Juanita frowned at the unruly childs. They don't belong on college campi, she thought. In the past month, she had been through several serieses of crisises directing these field trips. She quickly counted up the minimas of various items she would need to order from the campus restaurant for lunch.

1. _____ children _____   3. _____ series _____   5. _____ minimums _____

2. _____ campuses _____   4. _____ crises _____

Spelling Application

Listed below are ten additional words that fit the patterns you have learned. Read each crossword puzzle clue. Then determine which word matches the clue and write the word in the squares provided.

bacteria	clothes	fish	fruit	fungi
minuses	moose	news	sheep	women

Across

2. antlered animals
6. mushrooms
8. what you wear
9. a healthy snack

Down

1. adult females
3. current events
4. opposite of pluses
5. germs
6. creatures with gills
7. fleeced animals

Spelling Power

Unit 3 Review

Lessons 9–12
In each of the sentences below, find the misspelled word and circle it. Then write its correct spelling on the line provided.

1. This pair of shoes is one of the best (buyes) I ever made. — buys
2. There are three (categorys) of chocolate: good, better, and best. — categories
3. For many of us, teachers are our (hereos) — heroes
4. Stay away from (controversyal) subjects on a first date. — controversial
5. The (alumnuses) gathered under the tent for the awards ceremony. — alumni
6. All (memoes) should be typed neatly, with no mistakes. — memos
7. The college had two (campes) one for business and the other for arts and sciences. — campuses
8. Washington, D.C., is home to many nonprofit (agencys) — agencies
9. There were two (approachs) to getting the job done. — approaches
10. The boys (layed) their books down and forgot them. — laid

Follow the directions for each item below. Then write the word on the line provided.

11. Form the plural of *athletics*. — athletics
12. Form the plural of *handkerchief*. — handkerchiefs
13. Form the plural of *crisis*. — crises
14. Form the plural of *cuff*. — cuffs
15. Form the plural of *series*. — series

Draw a line through the word in each set that is spelled incorrectly. Then write the word correctly on the line provided.

16. betrayal ~~betrail~~ — betrayal
17. ~~defyance~~ defiance — defiance
18. envious ~~envyous~~ — envious
19. ~~fezs~~ fezes — fezes
20. guesses ~~guessus~~ — guesses

Spelling Power

Proofreading Application

Lessons 9–12

Read the newspaper article below. Find the twenty misspelled words and circle them. Then write the correct spellings of the words on the lines below the article.

Nature Preserve Celebrates Grand Opening

The Nature Preserve officially opened its gates this weekend in Island Park with a ceremony that featured two grand pianoes and a performance by the Island East Dance Company. The ceremony, which was broadcast on radioes throughout Atlantic County, was kicked off by a visit from Mayor Ramirez—who arrived on water skies producing huge splashs.

To generate excitement, the mayor and the executive board sported temporary tattooes of salmons, oxes, wolfs and other animals sheltered at the Nature Preserve. Scarfs with similar designs were being sold at the event to raise additional funds.

"We were overjoyd to open our doors this soon," said Executive Director Paula Strum. "Our funding has steadyly increased, which implys that the community is ready to welcome this sort of attraction. If the readyness is there, we know we will succeed and the animals will benefit."

The community came out in full force to attend the event. They enjoyed free refreshments, including tacoes, loafs of fresh bread, and a huge celebration cake. Childrens were entertained by a clown who made balloon animals.

According to Strum, the next step will be to catalog the animals in this natural wild habitat. The staff will be verifing dati, checking minimas, and comparing the numbers to national indexs.

For more information or to make a donation, contact the Nature Preserve at 1-800-555-1111.

1.	pianos	11.	steadily
2.	radios	12.	implies
3.	skis	13.	readiness
4.	splashes	14.	tacos
5.	tattoos	15.	loaves
6.	salmon	16.	Children
7.	oxen	17.	verifying
8.	wolves	18.	data
9.	Scarves	19.	minimums
10.	overjoyed	20.	indexes

Spelling Power

Lesson 13: Contractions

Word Bank

doesn't	he'd	I'll	it's	let's
might've	needn't	should've	they're	we're

Key Concepts

A contraction is a word that is created by combining two words, dropping one or more letters of the second word, and substituting an apostrophe for the dropped letter or letters. Following are some patterns in the formation of contractions that will help you understand and spell them correctly. Remember that the apostrophe replaces dropped letters.

1. Two words are joined together. For example, *does* and *not* becomes *doesnot.* Then the vowel in the second word is replaced by an apostrophe. *Doesnot* becomes *doesn't.* Other contractions that illustrate this pattern are *it's* (it is or it has), *let's* (let us), *needn't* (need not), *they're* (they are), and *we're* (we are).

2. Even when more than one letter is removed, a single apostrophe replaces the missing letters. For example, the words *might* and *have* become *mighthave.* Then the first two letters of *have* are replaced by an apostrophe. *Mighthave* becomes *might've.* Other illustrations of this pattern are *I'll* (I will), *it's* (it has), and *should've* (should have).

3. In contractions ending in *'d,* such as *he'd,* the *'d* can represent *would* or *had.*

4. Remember not to confuse *it's* with *its,* which is the possessive pronoun that means "belonging to it."

Spelling Practice

On the lines below, write the following word pairs as contractions.

1. let + us =   let's
2. they + are =   they're
3. it + is =   it's
4. does + not =   doesn't
5. I + will =   I'll

6. might + have =   might've
7. he + had =   he'd
8. need + not =   needn't
9. we + are =   we're
10. should + have =   should've

Spelling in Context

In the following sentences, find the misspelled word and circle it. Then write the correct spelling of the word.

1. (Its) ten o'clock and all is well.   It's
2. (Lets) have a picnic by the lake.   Let's
3. (Theyr'e) ready to leave when you are.   They're
4. We (should'ave) checked with you first.   should've
5. You (need'nt) worry about us.   needn't

LESSON 13 continued

Proofreading Practice

Read the paragraph below. Find the five misspelled words and circle them. Then write the correct spellings of the words on the lines below the paragraph.

"Ill use these," Ron thought as he reviewed the posters for the school election. "The picture doesnt look as good as it could, but wer'e not interested in paying an extra charge for reshooting it. I might'ave looked better if I hadn't smiled so broadly," he said to his mother. "Don't think that," she replied. He'ad had a beautiful smile.

1. I'll _____   4. might've _____

2. doesn't _____   5. He'd _____

3. we're _____

Spelling Application

Listed below are ten additional words that fit the patterns you have learned. Below the list are scrambled forms of the words. Unscramble each word and write it correctly on the line provided. Remember to add the apostrophe in the correct place.

aren't	couldn't	he'll	here's	she'll
we've	who's	who've	won't	you're

1. hesll   she'll _____

2. eevw   we've _____

3. lleh   he'll _____

4. sohw   who's _____

5. reouy   you're _____

6. ontw   won't _____

7. dtoucln   couldn't _____

8. tnrea   aren't _____

9. eeshr   here's _____

10. vehwo   who've _____

Spelling Power

Lesson 14: Possessives

Word Bank

All Souls' Day	bosses'	Charles Dickens's	children's	Father's Day
G.I.'s	household's	ours	public figure's	senators'

Key Concepts

A possessive is a word that indicates ownership by a person, place, or thing. For example, "the dog's collar" means "the collar that belongs to the dog." Possessives and contractions are easily confused. The context of the sentence in which the word appears indicates whether it is a possessive or a contraction. Use the following guidelines when spelling possessives.

1. A possessive generally contains an apostrophe, as in *children's.* Not all words with apostrophes are possessive, however; *it's* is the contraction for "it is" or "it has."

2. Possessive pronouns do not use an apostrophe, as in *ours* and *yours.*

3. Placement of the apostrophe changes depending on whether a possessive is singular or plural. If the item belongs to one person, place, or thing, the apostrophe comes before the *s,* even if the noun contains more than one word, as in *public figure's,* or is an abbreviation, as in *G.I.'s.* Note that the word *household* is singular, even though many people may be part of that group. Therefore, the possessive would be singular as well, as in *the household's budget.*

4. Place an apostrophe and *s* at the end of most proper names ending in *s,* as in *Charles Dickens's.*

5. If the plural of a noun ends in *s,* simply add an apostrophe to form the possessive, as in *bosses'* and *senators'.* If the plural does not end in *s,* add an apostrophe and *s,* as in *children's.*

6. The names of many holidays contain possessives. The possessive may be singular, as in *Father's Day,* or plural, as in *All Souls' Day.*

Spelling Practice

Listed below are seven spelling patterns. On the line below each pattern, write the word or words from the Word Bank to which it applies.

1. For singular nouns, add an apostrophe and *s.*

   G.I.'s   household's   public figure's

2. For plural nouns ending in s, add an apostrophe.

   bosses'   senators'

3. For plural nouns that do not end in *s,* add an apostrophe and *s.*

   children's

4. For proper nouns, add an apostrophe and *s.*

   Charles Dickens's

5. Possessive pronouns have no apostrophe.

   ours

6. The names of holidays may contain singular possessives.

   Father's Day

7. The names of holidays may contain plural possessives.

   All Souls' Day

LESSON 14 continued

Spelling in Context

Complete each sentence below with the correct word from the Word Bank.

1. The nanny picked up the ___children's___ toys.

2. The ___G.I.'s___ uniform had a camouflage pattern.

3. Many people find their ___bosses'___ demands to be unreasonable.

4. ___Father's Day___ is my favorite holiday because I like to spend time with my dad.

5. She visited her mother's grave each year on ___All Souls' Day___.

Proofreading Practice

Read the paragraph below. Find the five misspelled words and circle them. Then write the correct spellings of the words on the lines below the paragraph.

Wayne turned on the television to watch the senators's debate, but he soon turned it off in disgust. A public figures's opinion should be easier to understand, he thought. Wayne picked up a copy of Charles Dickens' *Great Expectations,* one of his favorite books. Just then the lights flickered and went out. Wayne sighed. "A households' electric supply should be better than this," he thought as he went in search of a flashlight. "No one on our block has service as poor as ours'."

1. ___senators'___   3. ___Charles Dickens's___   5. ___ours___

2. ___public figure's___   4. ___household's___

Spelling Application

Listed below are five additional words that fit the patterns you have learned. An apostrophe and the letter *s* have been provided for each word. Use the code to find the missing letters and build the pyramid.

businesswomen's   defendant's   duchess's   mourners'   sister-in-law's

CODE

a=4, b=21, c=7, d=18, e=15, f=20, g=11, h=23, i=24, j=5, k=12, l=3, m=25, n=2, o=13, p=17, q=16, r=10, s=8, t=6, u=1, v=9, w=19, x=22, y=26, z=14

				d	u	c	h	e	s	s	'	s
				18	1	7	23	15	8	8		
				m	o	u	r	n	e	r	s	'
				25	13	1	10	2	15	10		
		d	e	f	e	n	d	a	n	t	'	s
		18	15	20	15	2	18	4	2	6		
b	u	s	i	n	e	s	s	w	o	m	e	n	'	s
21	1	8	24	2	15	8	8	19	13	25	15	2		
s	i	s	t	e	r	-	i	n	-	l	a	w	'	s
8	24	8	6	15	10		24	2		3	4	19		

Spelling Power

Lesson 15: Syllabication
Word Bank

biology	cooperative	currency	demolition	digest
dinginess	election	hassle	intrusion	software

Key Concepts

Sounding out a multisyllable word can help you spell it. Say the word slowly. Listen to the way it breaks naturally into parts, or syllables. Then spell each syllable individually. This process often follows the patterns listed below. Listen to the sounds in each syllable as you study these words.

1. Compound words break into the words of which they are composed, as in *soft-ware.*
2. Prefixes and suffixes usually form separate syllables, as in *dem-o-li-tion, din-gi-ness, e-lec-tion,* and *in-tru-sion.*
3. A new syllable usually begins after a long vowel sound, as in *bi-ol-o-gy* and *di-gest.*
4. A single vowel sound may form its own syllable, as in *co-op-er-a-tive.*
5. A syllable with a short vowel sound usually ends with the consonant that follows the short vowel, as in *cur-ren-cy.*

Spelling Practice

Draw a line through the word in each set that is spelled incorrectly. Then write the word correctly.

1. ~~bialagy~~   demolition
   biology _____

2. hassle   ~~curency~~
   currency _____

3. ~~dijest~~   biology
   digest _____

4. ~~hasle~~   currency
   hassle _____

5. ~~softwear~~   digest
   software _____

6. ~~elecsion~~   dinginess
   election _____

7. cooperative   ~~intrution~~
   intrusion _____

8. ~~dingyness~~   software
   dinginess _____

9. ~~demolision~~   election
   demolition _____

10. intrusion   ~~cooprative~~
    cooperative _____

Spelling in Context

Complete each sentence with the correct word from the Word Bank.

1. The dollar is the __currency__ we use in the United States.

2. __Biology__ is my favorite science class.

3. The computer programmer recommended the new __software__ to her employer.

4. She hoped the child would be __cooperative__ and go to bed without a fuss.

5. It takes our bodies a long time to __digest__ meat.

LESSON 15 continued

Proofreading Practice

Read the paragraph below. Find the five misspelled words and circle them. Then write the correct spellings of the words on the lines below the paragraph.

Marty peeked into the room and withdrew because of its dingyness. A thick layer of dust covered the furniture. The cleaning crew would have to get everything back in order. What a hasle that would be! Despite all his years as a police officer, Marty couldn't help feeling that this intrution was unnecessary. Yet the tenants weren't taking care of the place, and someone had to do something. At least he'd prevent a demolision crew from getting to this building. Maybe his efforts would be remembered during his upcoming elecsion campaign.

1. dinginess
2. hassle
3. intrusion
4. demolition
5. election

Spelling Application

Listed below are ten additional words that fit the patterns you have learned. Read each crossword puzzle clue. Then determine which word matches the clue and write the word in the squares provided.

accounting	bobbin	boycott	coyness	curiosity
equipping	gallery	labor	priority	selection

Across
2. choice among several items
4. records of business dealings
5. a thirst for knowledge
6. a place where art is displayed
8. a part of a sewing machine
9. something important

Down
1. to take action against something
3. outfitting with equipment
5. the act of pretending to be shy
7. work

Spelling Power

Lesson 16: Soft Final Syllables

Word Bank

council	embezzle	infinitely	jersey	juror
pillar	restorer	scalpel	sulfur	tribal

Key Concepts

Some words end in soft final syllables that contain an indistinct vowel sound. This indistinct vowel sound is known as the *schwa* (ə). The schwa sound can be spelled many different ways. Try to visualize these words as you study.

1. Endings with the \ə\ sound may be spelled with seven different letter combinations: *al, el, il, ile, le, ol,* and *ul.* The most common endings are *al,* as in *tribal, el,* as in *scalpel,* and *le,* as in *embezzle.* The list of words using the other endings is small enough to commit to memory:

    consul, council, evil, fossil, fragile, idol, missile, mobile, pencil, pistol, stencil, symbol, tonsil.

2. Endings with the \ər\ sound have six possible letter combinations: *ar, er, or, re, ur,* and *yr.* The most common endings are *ar,* as in *pillar; er* as in *restorer;* and *or,* as in *juror.* Other words include *acre, martyr, murmur, occur,* and *sulfur.*

3. Words that end in a soft, or unstressed \ē\ sound may be spelled with *ey, ie,* or *y.* There are a few words that end in *ie* or *ey.* Commit this short list to memory. Recognizing these words will help you to spell other words ending in *y.*

    alley, brownie, collie, curtsey, donkey, hockey, infinitely, jersey, jockey, kidney, monkey, movie, paisley, parsley, prairie, turkey, valley

Spelling Practice

In each case below, decide which ending should be added to make a complete word. Then write the word on the line provided.

1. counc + (el, il) =
   council

2. scalp + (al, el) =
   scalpel

3. embezz + (el, le) =
   embezzle

4. trib + (al, le) =
   tribal

5. jur + (er, or) =
   juror

6. restor + (ar, er) =
   restorer

7. pill + (ar, or) =
   pillar

8. sulf + (er, ur) =
   sulfur

9. jers + (ey, ie) =
   jersey

10. infinite + (ley, ly) =
    infinitely

LESSON 16 continued

Spelling in Context

Decide which word from the Word Bank is described in each phrase below. Then write the word on the line.

1. a small, sharp knife used by surgeons   scalpel

2. a member of a jury   juror

3. a vertical column or building support   pillar

4. something belonging to a tribe   tribal

5. a mineral that is usually yellow in color   sulfur

Proofreading Practice

Read the paragraph below. Find the five misspelled words and circle them. Then write the correct spellings of the words on the lines below the paragraph.

Trying to ⟨embezzal⟩ funds from the student ⟨councel⟩ budget was no small affair. The students had worked hard to raise money to buy a new ⟨jersy⟩ for each football player. Now Stuart was faced with an ⟨infiniteley⟩ difficult decision. He could report the offenders, confront them, or ignore the situation. He decided on the first option, hoping to be the ⟨restorar⟩ of order.

1. embezzle   3. jersey   5. restorer

2. council   4. infinitely

Spelling Application

Listed below are five additional words that fit the patterns you have learned. Find them in the word maze and circle them. Then write the word that applies to each pattern.

cedar   diesel   fatal   genie   murmur

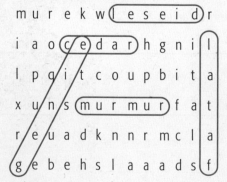

1. Pattern 1: \ər\ spelled as *ar.*   cedar

2. Pattern 2: \ər\ spelled as *ur.*   murmur

3. Pattern 3: \ə\ spelled as *al.*   fatal

4. Pattern 4: \ə\ spelled as *el.*   diesel

5. Pattern 5: \ē\ spelled as *ie.*   genie

Spelling Power

Unit 4 Review

Lessons 13–16
In each sentence below, find the misspelled word and circle it. Then write the correct spelling on the line provided.

1. Her (jersy) was soaked through by the rain.   jersey

2. The attorney asked for the (jurer) to be dismissed.   juror

3. The (G.I.s) uniform was neatly pressed.   G.I.'s

4. Our (households') income is $50,000 per year.   household's

5. The employees were jealous that their (bosse's) offices were so much larger than their own.   bosses'

6. My two (senator's) opinions on the issue were very different.   senators'

7. She paused for a minute, attempting to (dijest) the surprising news.   digest

8. I never speak to telephone salespeople because I resent the (intrution) on my privacy.   intrusion

9. We were relieved to see that the unstable building had been scheduled for (demalition)   demolition

10. The (sulfer) in the water released a strong smell.   sulfur

Listed below are five words that are missing apostrophes. Write the correct spelling of each word on the line provided.

11. neednt   needn't

12. were   we're

13. Ill   I'll

14. theyre   they're

15. Fathers Day   Father's Day

Draw a line through the word in each set that is spelled incorrectly. Then write the word correctly on the line provided.

16. software   ~~softwear~~   software

17. ~~embezzel~~   embezzle   embezzle

18. ~~dingyness~~   dinginess   dinginess

19. ~~trible~~   tribal   tribal

20. restorer   ~~restoror~~   restorer

Spelling Power

Proofreading Application

Lessons 13–16
Read the letter below. Find the twenty misspelled words and circle them. Then write the correct spellings of the words on the lines below the letter.

June 1, 2000

To the members of the school board:

I wish to file a formal letter of complaint about the school board's handling of several major issues. First, I learned that the board has slashed the budget for the advanced (biolagy) program at the high school. Even one less (scalple) in the science lab shortchanges our students. Surely the small amount of (curency) spent on this program is worth the investment.

The all-day celebration of homecoming at the high school was also an error in judgment. (Its) an extracurricular activity that (neednt) detract from the regular schedule. The administration (shoul'dve) remembered that academics take first priority.

Finally, I am outraged that a number of literary classics, including (Charles Dickens) *Oliver Twist,* have been removed from the library's shelves because of "offensive" content. (Doesnt) the literary merit of these books outweigh the need to "protect" our (childrens') minds from serious issues?

I have attempted to raise my concerns at an open meeting of the town (councel) but the members of the board were not (cooprative.) It's (infiniteley) upsetting to me that a trustee of the school district would have so little regard for the concerns of ordinary families such as (ours'.) A (public figures') actions should reflect his status as a (piller) of our community.

(Lets) take the time to discuss these issues before the next (electian.) I do not wish to (hasle) the board. Please take time to (dijest) what I've said, and then we can (laber) over a solution.

Sincerely,
Doris M. Loper

1.	biology	11.	cooperative
2.	scalpel	12.	infinitely
3.	currency	13.	ours
4.	It's	14.	public figure's
5.	needn't	15.	pillar
6.	should've	16.	Let's
7.	Charles Dickens's	17.	election
8.	Doesn't	18.	hassle
9.	children's	19.	digest
10.	council	20.	labor

Spelling Power

Lesson 17: Prefixes

Word Bank

accumulation	antiseptic	biannual	confirm	disinherit
monotony	prearranged	revert	subhuman	unity

Key Concepts

A prefix is a syllable that can be added to the beginning of a word or a word root. Adding a prefix typically alters the meaning of the original word or word root. Try to visualize these common words as you study them.

1. Knowing the meaning of a prefix can help you learn the meaning of a word with that prefix. For example, if you know that *sub-* means "below," you can guess that *subhuman* means "inferior to a human." The prefix *pre-* means "before," so *prearranged* means "arranged ahead."

2. A prefix can have more than one meaning. The prefix *re-* can mean "return or go back" or "again." *Revert* means "return to previous behavior," while *relocate* means "to locate again."

3. Adding a prefix to a word usually does not change the word's original spelling.

    anti + septic = antiseptic   bi + annual = biannual   dis + inherit = disinherit

4. When a prefix comes before a word root that cannot stand alone, the spelling of the original word root is usually not affected.

    mono + tony = monotony   uni + ty = unity

5. In some cases, however, adding a prefix to a word does require a change in the spelling of the prefix.

    com + firm = confirm   ad + cumulation = accumulation

Spelling Practice

Combine each word or word root and prefix below and write the new word on the line provided.

1. ad + cumulation =
   accumulation

2. uni + ty =
   unity

3. dis + inherit =
   disinherit

4. pre + arranged =
   prearranged

5. mono + tony =
   monotony

6. anti + septic =
   antiseptic

7. bi + annual =
   biannual

8. com + firm =
   confirm

9. re + vert =
   revert

10. sub + human =
   subhuman

LESSON 17 continued

Spelling in Context

Add a prefix to each word or word root below to make one of the words from the Word Bank.

1. firm _____confirm_____
2. inherit _____disinherit_____
3. annual _____biannual_____

4. arranged _____prearranged_____
5. human _____subhuman_____

Proofreading Practice

Read the paragraph below. Find the five misspelled words and circle them. Then write the correct spellings of the word on the lines below the paragraph.

The acumulation of snow was unbelievable. Shayna smelled the anteseptic solution from the hospital corridor. She hated the monatony and wanted to reevert to being a kid–to build a snowman–but she knew that until her injury healed, there would be little unety between dreams and reality.

1. _____accumulation_____
2. _____antiseptic_____
3. _____monotony_____

4. _____revert_____
5. _____unity_____

Spelling Application

Listed below are five additional words that fit the patterns you have learned. Find them in the word maze and circle them. Then write the words or words from the maze to which each pattern applies.

assort   condense   disability   relocate   submerge

```
s d k j a c f n o c
u i a s s o r t l o
b s f k u n v s j n
y t i l i b a s i d
r a r e l o c a t e
f s u b m e r g e n
e e j d m x v e w s
a s d k u r c q p e
```

1. Pattern 1: Sometimes adding a prefix changes the spelling of the prefix. _____assort_____

2. Pattern 2: Change the prefix *com-* to *con-* before a consonant. _____condense_____

3. Pattern 3: The spellings of the prefix and the original word do not change.

_____disability_____   _____relocate_____   _____submerge_____

Spelling Power

Lesson 18: The Suffixes -*ance, -ence, -ant, -ent*

Word Bank

acceptance	brilliant	circumference	defendant	evident
hesitant	prominent	radiance	reference	resistance

Key Concepts

A suffix is a syllable that can be added to the end of a word. Like prefixes, suffixes have their own meanings, so adding a suffix to a word changes the meaning or function of the original word. This lesson explores four common suffixes: -*ance, -ence, -ant,* and -*ent.* Because the spelling of words with these suffixes can be confusing, try to visualize the words as you study them.

1. The suffixes -*ance* and -*ence* both mean "the quality of" and are used to create nouns. For example, *resistance* means "the quality or state of resisting."

2. Because -*ance* and -*ence* are pronounced the same way, you will have to commit to memory the words that use these endings. Examples are *acceptance, radiance, circumference,* and *reference.*

3. Adding the suffixes -*ant* or -*ent* to words can create either nouns or adjectives. When used to create nouns, -*ant* and -*ent* refer to a person or thing that has the characteristic of the word root. For example, *defendant* means "one who defends or is defended."

4. When used to create adjectives, the suffixes -*ant* and -*ent* refer to a person, place, or thing "that does" or "that shows" the action of the word root. For example, *hesitant* means "hesitating."

5. The suffixes -*ant* and -*ent* are pronounced the same way. Becoming familiar with words that use these endings is the best way to learn how to spell them. Examples are *brilliant, evident,* and *prominent.*

Spelling Practice

Draw a line through the word in each set that is spelled incorrectly. Then write the word correctly on the line.

1. resistance   ~~resistence~~   resistance
2. ~~circumferance~~   circumference   circumference
3. ~~defendent~~   defendant   defendant
4. ~~evidant~~   evident   evident
5. radiance   ~~radience~~   radiance
6. ~~referance~~   reference   reference
7. ~~prominant~~   prominent   prominent
8. acceptance   ~~acceptence~~   acceptance
9. brilliant   ~~brillient~~   brilliant
10. hesitant   ~~hesitent~~   hesitant

Name _____ Date _____ Class _____

LESSON 18 continued

Spelling in Context

Complete each sentence with the correct word from the Word Bank.

1. The __brilliant__ scientist helped discover a cure for cancer.

2. There is a geometric formula to find the __circumference__ of a circle.

3. A dictionary is a valuable __reference__ book.

4. She was __hesitant__ to confide in him because he had never kept a secret.

5. The __defendant__ pleaded his case before the judge.

Proofreading Practice

Read the paragraph below. Find the five misspelled words and circle them. Then write the correct spellings of the words on the lines below the paragraph.

Maria Lopez walked proudly to center stage. Her confident attitude gave her an inner radience. As a prominant attorney, she rarely had the chance to address a group of students and she relished this opportunity. Yet she could sense the resistence. After all, she would be addressing a very controversial topic–drug abuse. It was evidant that she would have to work to win acceptence.

1. radiance
2. prominent
3. resistance
4. evident
5. acceptance

Spelling Application

Listed below are five additional words that fit the patterns you have learned. The suffixes have been provided in the word pyramid. Use the code to find the missing letters and build the pyramid. Then write the words on the lines below.

ignorant   independent   insurance   negligence   patience

CODE
a=13, b=21, c=19, d=11, e=6, f=14, g=8, h=23, i=24, j=17, k=15, l=7, m=25, n=5, o=16, p=10, q=9, r=2, s=20, t=18, u=4, v=1, w=12, x=3, y=26, z=22

1. ignorant
2. patience
3. insurance
4. negligence
5. independent

i	g	n	o	r	a	n	t
24	8	5	16	2			

p	a	t	i	e	n	c	e
10	13	18	24				

i	n	s	u	r	a	n	c	e
24	5	20	4	2				

n	e	g	l	i	g	e	n	c	e
5	6	8	7	24	8				

i	n	d	e	p	e	n	d	e	n	t
24	5	11	6	10	6	5	11			

Spelling Power

Lesson 19: The Suffixes -ize, -ise, -yze

Word Bank

compromise	criticize	economize	exercise	organize
revolutionize	socialize	supervise	symbolize	visualize

Key Concepts

The suffixes -ize, -ise, and -yze can be added to some words or word roots to create verbs that mean "to make" or "to become." Try to visualize these words as you study them.

1. The ending -ize is the most commonly used suffix in this group. It is often added when the original word or word root ends in a consonant, as in *criticize, organize, revolutionize, socialize, symbolize,* and *visualize.*

2. If the word or word root ends in *y,* the *y* may be deleted before adding -ize. For example, drop the *y* in *economy* before adding the -ize ending to form *economize.*

3. The suffix -ise often follows the letters *c, m, v,* and *pr,* as in *compromise, exercise,* and *supervise.*

4. Only a few verbs end in -yze. Commit words such as *analyze* and *paralyze* to memory.

Spelling Practice

Decide which suffix (-ize, -ise, or -yze) should be added to each word or word root to make a new word. Then write the complete word on the line provided.

1. econom   economize
2. critic   criticize
3. social   socialize
4. exerc   exercise
5. visual   visualize

6. revolution   revolutionize
7. organ   organize
8. superv   supervise
9. comprom   compromise
10. symbol   symbolize

Spelling in Context

Decide which word from the Word Bank is defined in each phrase below. Then write the word on the line provided.

1. to oversee   supervise

2. to put in order   organize

3. to find fault with   criticize

4. to form a mental picture of   visualize

5. to use signs to represent something; to stand for symbolize

LESSON 19 continued

Proofreading Practice

Read the paragraph below. Find the five misspelled words and circle them. Then write the correct spellings of the words on the lines below the paragraph.

When Rick, the owner of a local gymnasium, decided to make some major changes, his partners were timid. They wanted him to economise. He disagreed, saying that his ideas would revolutionise the notion of "being fit." His plans included adding a restaurant where people could socialyze after they exercized. The partners agreed to compromize. They decided to offer juices and health drinks rather than full meals.

1. economize
2. revolutionize
3. socialize

4. exercised
5. compromise

Spelling Application

Listed below are ten additional words that fit the patterns you have learned. Read each crossword puzzle clue. Then determine which word matches the clue and write the word in the squares provided.

advise	despise	disguise	energize	idolize
recognize	revise	surprise	summarize	sympathize

Across
1. to create the unexpected
3. to hate
4. to worship
6. to create momentum or energy
8. to mask
9. to identify

Down
1. to restate, generally in shorter form
2. to offer sympathy
5. to counsel or offer wisdom
7. to make changes or alterations

Spelling Power

Lesson 20: Word Roots

Word Bank

biography	geology	hydraulic	missile	persist
prescribe	sophisticated	transcript	transfer	transmit

Key Concepts

Word roots contain the basic meanings of words. Some word roots, such as *pose* and *scribe,* are complete words. Others need prefixes and suffixes. Many prefixes and suffixes can be added to word roots without altering the spelling of the word roots, as in *prescribe.* Sometimes changes have to be made. For example, to add the suffix *-ive* to the word root *pense,* drop the *e* in *pense* to create *pensive.* Learning the spellings of word roots will help you master the spelling of words that contain them.

1. The word roots *sist* (to stand) and *fer* (to carry) are Latin. A word root may need a prefix to form a word, as in *persist* and *transfer.*

2. The Latin word root *miss/mit* means "to send." It is used in many words, such as *missile* and *transmit.*

3. The Latin word root *scribe/script* means "to write." The *scribe* word root is used in verbs such as *prescribe. Script* is used in nouns such as *transcript.* The Greek word root *graph* also means "to write." It appears in words such as in *biography.*

4. The Greek word root *soph* means "wise," as in *sophisticated.*

5. The Greek word root *hydr* means "water," as in *hydraulic.*

6. The Greek word root *logy* means "the study of," as in *geology.*

Spelling Practice

Draw a line through the word in each set that is spelled incorrectly. Then write the word correctly on the line provided.

1. prescribe ~~hidraulic~~ _____hydraulic_____

2. persist ~~biograffy~~ _____biography_____

3. ~~misile~~ geology _____missile_____

4. hydraulic ~~transferr~~ _____transfer_____

5. ~~sofisticated~~ transcript _____sophisticated_____

6. missile ~~transmiss~~ _____transmit_____

7. ~~transkript~~ transfer _____transcript_____

8. sophisticated ~~percist~~ _____persist_____

9. ~~prescripe~~ transmit _____prescribe_____

10. biography ~~geolagy~~ _____geology_____

LESSON 20 continued

Spelling in Context

Complete each sentence below with the correct word from the Word Bank.

1. The world leaders decided to destroy the ___missile___ silos as a sign of peace.

2. Martha enjoyed the latest ___biography___ of Abraham Lincoln.

3. The workers used the ___hydraulic___ lift to reach the high shelves.

4. Debra asked the doctor to ___prescribe___ an antibiotic for her infection.

5. Reggie wanted an outfit that would make him feel ___sophisticated___.

Proofreading Practice

Read the paragraph below. Find the five misspelled words and circle them. Then write the correct spellings of the words on the lines below the paragraph.

Helen wanted to (transffer) into an advanced (geolegy) class. Mr. Hayes, her college advisor, argued against it, but Helen decided to (percist.) She offered to (transmitt) to him a (transcrip) of her grades. When Mr. Hayes saw Helen's grades in related courses, he was convinced that she would do well.

1. ___transfer___
2. ___geology___
3. ___persist___
4. ___transmit___
5. ___transcript___

Spelling Application

Listed below are ten additional words that fit the patterns you have learned. Below the list are scrambled forms of the words. Unscramble each word and write it correctly on the line provided.

autograph   concise   dismissal   ecology   hydrant
pensive   persist   philosopher   prefer   transmission

1. spenvie
   ___pensive___

2. touargpah
   ___autograph___

3. sseirtp
   ___persist___

4. antryhd
   ___hydrant___

5. rtnassimsino
   ___transmission___

6. eoogcly
   ___ecology___

7. sidmisals
   ___dismissal___

8. oesccni
   ___concise___

9. rrepfe
   ___prefer___

10. ehoiposplrh
   ___philosopher___

Spelling Power

Unit 5 Review

Lessons 17–20

In each sentence below, find the misspelled word and circle it. Then write its correct spelling on the line provided.

1. The (exercize) routine was very strenuous for those who had not been active.   exercise

2. The (radience) of the moon lit the night sky.   radiance

3. My thesaurus is the one (referance) tool I cannot do without.   reference

4. Theresa felt so strongly about the issue that she could not (compromize).   compromise

5. The mediator offered to (prearange) for a neutral meeting place.   prearrange

6. She measured the circle's (circumferance) and wrote the figure in her notebook.   circumference

7. His description helped us (visualise) the seacoast in our minds.   visualize

8. The (defendent) stood tall in the courtroom as the verdict was read.   defendant

9. I hope that Joseph doesn't (reevert) to his old habit of snacking on fatty foods.   revert

10. If I do not (organise) my closet, I will not be able to find anything to wear.   organize

Decide which word from the Word Banks in the four preceding lessons is defined in each phrase below. Then write the word on the line provided.

11. to cut back on spending   economize

12. to turn something over to someone   transfer

13. to oversee   supervise

14. to mix with friends   socialize

15. a written report or record   transcript

Draw a line through the word in each set that is spelled incorrectly. Then write the word correctly on the line provided.

16. symbolize   ~~symbolise~~   symbolize

17. ~~misille~~   missile   missile

18. disinherit   ~~disinheritt~~   disinherit

19. geology   ~~geolagy~~   geology

20. hydraulic   ~~hidralic~~   hydraulic

Spelling Power

Proofreading Application

Lessons 17–20
Read the magazine article below. Find the twenty misspelled words and circle them. Then write the correct spellings of the words on the lines below the article.

Scientists Continue Search for Cure for Cancer

Prominant scientific researchers continue to work to find a cure for cancer. They are hesitent to make any claim until they can comfirm their findings. Important discoveries are usually the acumulation of many years of sophisticatd research by brillient scientists. These dedicated detectives percist in hunting down all leads. They transmitt their findings for publication only when it is evidant that they have made a breakthrough.

One scientist has found a link between subbhuman particles within normal cells and cancer cells. The discovery was made while the scientist was working with an anteseptic solution. Now that the substance has been identified, the scientist is hoping to create a vaccine. He hopes that one day doctors can prescript this vaccine for their patients. The scientist spoke of the monotoney of the years of research and how that effort had finally yielded a promising result. According to his biograffy published by the research institute, this scientist has been working in the field for twenty years. He is hoping that his findings will revolutionise the treatment of cancer.

The announcement of this discovery was made at the biennual meeting of the cancer research community. Some scientists critise the announcement and offer resistence to the discovery. They want to take time to analyze the results carefully. The researcher who made the discovery is confident of acceptence of his findings by his colleagues. He noted that there is unety of purpose in the search for a cure.

1.	Prominent	11.	antiseptic
2.	hesitant	12.	prescribe
3.	confirm	13.	monotony
4.	accumulation	14.	biography
5.	sophisticated	15.	revolutionize
6.	brilliant	16.	biannual
7.	persist	17.	criticize
8.	transmit	18.	resistance
9.	evident	19.	acceptance
10.	subhuman	20.	unity

Spelling Power

Lesson 21: Noun Suffixes

Word Bank

accuracy	cowardice	criticism	division	gratitude
optician	politician	possession	reality	superstition

Key Concepts

A suffix is an ending that can be added to a word to form another word with a different meaning or function. Sometimes a word's existing ending must be dropped or changed so that a suffix can be added. Adding a suffix to a word often changes it from one part of speech to another. To help identify and spell nouns, keep the following suffixes and their meanings in mind. Then try to visualize these words as you study them.

1. The suffix *-tion* has the sound \shən\ or \chən\. It indicates an action, condition, process, or result, as in *superstition*.

2. The suffix *-sion* has the sound \shən\ or \zhən\. It also indicates an action, condition, process, or result, as in *possession* and *division*.

3. The suffix *-ity* means "the state or the condition of being a certain way," as in *reality*.

4. The suffixes *-cy* and *-y* indicate qualities or actions, as in *accuracy* and *inquiry*.

5. The suffixes *-ician, -er, -or,* and *-ist* indicate a person who does or is skilled in something, as in *optician* and *politician*.

6. The suffix *-ism* indicates an action, result, or condition, as in *criticism*.

7. The suffixes *-tude* and *-ice* express abstract qualities or ideas, as in *cowardice* and *gratitude*.

Spelling Practice

Combine each word and suffix below to form a noun. Write the new word on the line provided.

1. grateful + tude = _gratitude_   6. coward + ice = _cowardice_

2. political + ian = _politician_   7. optic + ian = _optician_

3. real + ity = _reality_   8. accurate + cy = _accuracy_

4. superstitious + tion = _superstition_   9. critical + ism = _criticism_

5. possess + ion = _possession_   10. divide + sion = _division_

Spelling in Context

Decide which word from the Word Bank is defined in each phrase below. Then write the word.

1. person who is involved in politics _politician_

2. the opposite of fantasy _reality_

3. something that is owned, occupied, or controlled _possession_

4. quality of being thankful _gratitude_

5. the process of breaking something down into parts _division_

Name _____ Date _____ Class _____

LESSON 21 continued

Proofreading Practice

Read the paragraph below. Find the five misspelled words and circle them. Then write the correct spellings of the words on the lines below the paragraph.

Dorothy's fear of an old superstision haunted her all day. She had cracked her mirrored sunglasses, and she knew that bad luck would follow. Not even the criticizm of the optishun who replaced her lenses changed her mind. She believed in the accuricy of the prediction beyond any doubt and decided to hide in her house until the bad luck hit. Just before twilight, her vigil of cowardace ended when she spilled grape juice on her favorite white sweater. She could relax!

1. superstition

2. criticism

3. optician

4. accuracy

5. cowardice

Spelling Application   These answers may appear in any order.

Listed below are five additional words that use the noun suffixes you have learned. Find them in the word maze and circle them. Then write the words from the maze on the lines provided.

attitude   civilization   democracy   mathematician   patriotism

```
p m s c f t y u j m n p h f r
l c a x s e r i s o d t o l n
e r u t j n i i q b r d w a
a y b s h l t s r n w i h u i
t g d e m o c r a c y r n e c
q h e t i q m o s f h k d x i
n r w r s y i a p s f u e g t
z c t s b m w e t f t a m t a
l a r l p e b l e i g e o p m
p m i e t y y u t h c a c l e
u c s z f i p t m r w i r v h
g m w e g m a s i t b n a c t
r f b j i o m g r w a x c n a
s c i v i l i z a t i o n t m
```

1. democracy

2. civilization

3. patriotism

4. attitude

5. mathematician

Spelling Power

Lesson 22: Adjective Suffixes

Word Bank

cautious	dangerous	delicious	desirable	famous
horrible	laughable	legible	navigable	permissible

Key Concepts

A suffix is an ending that can be added to a word to form a new word with a different meaning or function. Sometimes a word's existing ending must be dropped or changed so that a suffix can be added. Adding a suffix to a word often changes it from one part of speech to another. When adding a suffix to a word to form a descriptive adjective, keep the following suffixes and their meanings in mind. Then visualize each word to help you recall its spelling.

1. The suffix -ous is added to complete nouns to form adjectives that mean "full of" or "characterized by." If the noun ends in silent e, drop the e before adding the suffix.

    danger + ous = dangerous   fame + ous = famous

2. Words ending with the suffixes -cious and -tious should be committed to memory. Both suffixes are pronounced as \shəs\, as in *delicious* and *cautious*.

3. The suffix -able is added to a complete verb, a verb that ends in a silent e that has been dropped, or a word root that ends in a hard c or g to form an adjective. It means "able" or "capable of being." Examples include *laughable, desirable,* and *navigable.*

4. The suffix -ible is added to a word root that ends in ss, a word root that ends in a soft c or g, or a word root that is not a complete word. Its meaning is the same as -able. Examples include *permissible, legible,* and *horrible.*

Spelling Practice

Listed below are ten spelling patterns. On the line following each pattern, write the word from the Word Bank to which the pattern applies.

1. Add -able if a word ends in a hard c or g.   navigable

2. Add -ible to word roots that end in ss.   permissible

3. Commit to memory the letter patterns of words ending with the suffix -tious.   cautious

4. If a noun ends in a silent e, drop the e before adding -ous.   famous

5. Commit to memory the spelling of words ending with the suffix -cious.   delicious

6. Add -ous to nouns that are whole words.   dangerous

7. Add -able if the word root is a complete word.   laughable

8. Add -ible if the word ends in a soft g.   legible

9. Add -able if the word ends in a silent e that has been dropped.   desirable

10. Add -ible if the word root is not a complete word.   horrible

LESSON 22 continued

Spelling in Context

Complete each sentence with the correct word from the Word Bank.

1. The celebrity was too _famous_ to be able to go anywhere unnoticed.

2. Because her writing was barely _legible_, no one could read her note.

3. The river was not _navigable_ because it was not deep enough.

4. The house I looked at today was less _desirable_ than the others because it was located near a noisy airport.

5. That restaurant serves _delicious_ pie that lures customers from all over.

Proofreading Practice

Read the paragraph below. Find the five misspelled words and circle them. Then write the correct spellings of the words on the lines below the paragraph.

Tyler's experience on Saturday was (horrable) not (laughible) It was not (permissable) for Tyler to cross the (dangeruous) stream by himself. He began by stepping in a (causious) way from stone to stone, but his foot slipped on some moss. Down he went into the cold stream. Although he could swim well and got out safely, Tyler told himself he would never make such a foolish decision again.

1. _horrible_   3. _permissible_   5. _cautious_

2. _laughable_   4. _dangerous_

Spelling Application

Listed below are five additional words that fit the patterns you have learned. Several suffixes have been provided in the word pyramid. Use the code to find the missing letters and build the pyramid. Then write the words on the lines provided.

furious   responsible   spacious   terrible   unbearable

CODE
a=23, b=2, c=20, d=8, e=11, f=6, g=16, h=4, i=3,
j=22, k=15, l=24, m=2, n=25, o=14, p=9, q=10, r=17,
s=19, t=21, u=26, v=18, w=7, x=1, y=12, z=13

1. _furious_

2. _spacious_

3. _terrible_

4. _unbearable_

5. _responsible_

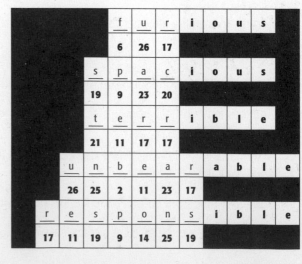

Spelling Power

Lesson 23: Verb Suffixes

Word Bank

clarify	congregate	deepen	designate	humidify
intensify	liberate	stupefy	tolerate	widen

Key Concepts

The addition of some suffixes changes a word or a word root into a verb. To identify and spell verbs, keep the following common verb suffixes in mind. Note that not every word root can stand without a suffix. For example, the word *congregate* without the -*ate* suffix is not a complete word.

1. The suffix -*ate* means "to make," "to become," or "to form," as in the words *congregate*, *liberate*, and *tolerate*. When adding -*ate* to a complete word that ends in a consonant, simply add the suffix, as in *designate*.

2. The suffix -*en* means "to become" or "to cause to be." Adjectives can sometimes be changed to verbs by adding -*en*, as in *deepen*. If there is a silent *e* at the end of the word root, drop the *e* and add -*en*.

3. The suffix -*fy* means "to make" or "to produce." If the word root ends in a consonant, an *i* is usually added before the suffix, as in *humidify* and *clarify*. Sometimes an *e* comes before the -*fy*, as in *stupefy*.

4. If a word root ends in a silent *e*, the *e* is usually replaced with an *i* before adding -*fy*, as in *intensify*.

Spelling Practice

In each case below, decide which suffix should be added to make a word. Then write the new word.

1. humid + (fy, en) =
   humidify

2. wide + (en, ate) =
   widen

3. clarity + (ate, fy) =
   clarify

4. design + (en, ate) =
   designate

5. tolerable + (fy, ate) =
   tolerate

6. intense + (fy, en) =
   intensify

7. stupid + (ate, fy) =
   stupefy

8. deep + (en, fy) =
   deepen

9. congregation + (fy, ate) =
   congregate

10. liberal + (ate, en) =
    liberate

Spelling in Context

Decide which word from the Word Bank is defined in each phrase below. Then write the word.

1. to fill the air with moisture   humidify

2. to collect or gather   congregate

LESSON 23 continued

3. to set aside for a special purpose   designate _____

4. to make dull or deprive of sensation   stupefy _____

5. to set free   liberate _____

Proofreading Practice

Read the paragraph below. Find the five misspelled words and circle them. Then write the correct spellings of the words on the lines below the paragraph.

     Tasha's series of failed experiments began to upset her, but her supervisor told her that a chemist had to be able to tolarate failure. She was not successful in her attempts to clarefy where she was making her mistakes. She knew she would have to intensefy her efforts and widin her research, but working through the weekend just caused Tasha's frustration to deepin.

1. tolerate _____   **3.** intensify _____   **5.** deepen _____

2. clarify _____   **4.** widen _____

Spelling Application   These answers may appear in any order.

Listed below are five additional words that use the verb suffixes you have learned. Find them in the word maze and circle them. Then write the words from the maze on the lines provided.

     circulate   glorify   heighten   qualify   roughen

```
m o n q r s t a c n i l h y
i k a u y n c x w a d n g p
z v m a e y i w a d c g u i
l x s l g u r l m z w q v c
t u f i f i c t h n k h i r
x w f f r o u g h e n s i a
y w a y b w l b l i m l o r
n o t q u s a d e o s e r v
e s a l i m t m d t r z o s
h e i g h t e n o f t i n v
m d c w a c l t x v t l f a
g b c z u s a c n b r z i y
```

1. qualify _____   **3.** roughen _____   **5.** glorify _____

2. heighten _____   **4.** circulate _____

Spelling Power

Lesson 24: Adverb Suffixes

Word Bank

automatically	clockwise	dully	endways	heavenward
knowingly	ordinarily	regretfully	reliably	spryly

Key Concepts

The addition of some suffixes changes a word or a word root into an adverb. To identify and spell adverbs, keep the following patterns in mind. Visualize these words as you study them.

1. The suffix -*ward* means "in the direction," as in *heavenward*. The suffix -*wise* means "in the manner," as in *clockwise*. The suffix -*ways* may have the same definition as -*ward* or -*wise*, as in *endways*.
2. The suffix -*ly* means "in a particular manner" or "to a particular extent." The suffix -*ly* can be added to many word roots to form adverbs without changing spelling, as in *knowingly*.
3. To add -*ly* to a word that ends in a consonant + *le*, drop the *le*, as in *reliably*.
4. If an adjective ends in *ic*, add -*ally* to form an adverb, as in *automatically*.
5. If a word ends with a single *l*, add -*ly* to form an adverb, as in *regretfully*.
6. If a word ends in a double *l*, drop the final *l* when adding -*ly*, as in *dully*.
7. Generally, for a one-syllable word that ends in a consonant + *y*, simply add -*ly*, as in *spryly*.
8. In a word of more than one syllable that ends with a consonant + *y*, change the *y* to *i* before adding -*ly*, as in *ordinarily*.

Spelling Practice

Combine each word and suffix below and write the new word on the line provided.

1. end + ways = _endways_
2. dull + ly = _dully_
3. knowing + ly = _knowingly_
4. regretful + ly = _regretfully_
5. reliable + ly = _reliably_
6. automatic + ally = _automatically_
7. clock + wise = _clockwise_
8. ordinary + ly = _ordinarily_
9. spry + ly = _spryly_
10. heaven + ward = _heavenward_

Spelling in Context

In each sentence below, find the misspelled word and circle it. Then write the word correctly.

1. The directions said to wind the toy (clockwize.)   _clockwise_
2. The preacher cast his eyes (heavenword) after his sermon was finished.   _heavenward_
3. We can count on the paper carrier to (reliably) deliver the paper on time.   _reliably_
4. The stars shone so (duly) that Irma put away her telescope.   _dully_
5. She set the box down (endway) instead of flat as instructed, so the dishes broke.   _endways_

LESSON 24 continued

Proofreading Practice

Read the paragraph below. Find the five misspelled words and circle them. Then write the correct spellings of the words on the lines below the paragraph.

(Ordinaryly) Guido would not have thought twice about the visitor looking around the farm. However, the stranger attracted attention when he (sprily) ran away from the horse stalls. When Guido (automaticly) shouted a greeting to him, the stranger hurried to his car and sped away. This behavior made Guido suspicious, and he reported the incident to his father. His father nodded (knowinly) and decided (regretfuly) to send Bell Boy, the favorite to win the Kentucky Derby, to his sister's ranch until after the race.

1. Ordinarily

2. spryly

3. automatically

4. knowingly

5. regretfully

Spelling Application

Listed below are ten additional words that fit the patterns you have learned. Read each crossword puzzle clue. Then determine which word matches the clue and write the word in the squares provided.

| carefully | fully | heartily | leisurely | otherwise |
| possibly | readily | shyly | skyward | terrifically |

Across

3. slowly
5. magnificently
7. completely
9. in the direction of the clouds
10. cautiously

Down

1. perhaps
2. bashfully
4. in a different way
6. willingly
8. with enthusiasm

Spelling Power

Spelling Power

Unit 6 Review

Lessons 21–24
Decide which suffix should be added to each word or word root to make a new word. Then write the new word on the line provided.

1. laugh + (able, ible) = _____laughable_____
2. leg + (able, ible) = _____legible_____
3. dull + (ally, ly) = _____dully_____
4. fame + (ious, ous) = _____famous_____
5. horr + (able, ible) = _____horrible_____

Draw a line through the word in each set that is spelled incorrectly. Then write the word correctly on the line provided.

6. ~~sprily~~   intensify   _____spryly_____
7. congregate   ~~realety~~   _____reality_____
8. ordinarily   ~~endwaze~~   _____endways_____
9. ~~critcisim~~   permissible   _____criticism_____
10. ~~heavnward~~   accuracy   _____heavenward_____

In each sentence below, find the misspelled word and circle it. Then write the correct spelling on the line provided.

11. The lack of oxygen appeared to (stupfiy) the climbers, who became disoriented and tired.   _____stupefy_____
12. You must visit the (optican) to get a new pair of glasses.   _____optician_____
13. The principal said that she would (tolereat) no interruptions.   _____tolerate_____
14. If you hold the jar while I turn the lid (clockways) we might be able to open it.   _____clockwise_____
15. Although everyone liked the (politition) no one voted for him.   _____politician_____
16. Intelligence is a (desirible) quality in a study partner.   _____desirable_____
17. You will need to (humidefy) your room in order to get rid of that cough.   _____humidify_____
18. He was successful on his third attempt to (liberaet) the hostages.   _____liberate_____
19. It is a common (superstician) that breaking a mirror brings bad luck.   _____superstition_____
20. It was difficult to feel sympathy for characters who displayed such (cowardis).   _____cowardice_____

Spelling Power

Proofreading Application

Lessons 21–24
Read the body of the memo from the class president to parents. Find the twenty misspelled words and circle them. Then write the correct spellings of the words on the lines below the memo.

I would like to introduce myself as the new freshman class president. My intention is to (reliablely) represent my class and to (deepin) the relationship between home and school.

Fund-Raising Activities

The class would like to extend its (gratitued) to all who participated in the bake sale. The community and class members baked many (delitious) foods. After the (divition) of the profit, the food pantry and the homeless shelter each received two hundred dollars. Please let us know of any other worthwhile local causes. We would never (knowingally) pass up the chance to help our town.

The ninth grade class (automaticaly) receives a percentage of the profit of the school magazine drive. They will use this and other funds in their (possesion) to help finance the first freshman dance.

Social Activities

The administration is asking students and parents to (congregat) in the stadium on Thursday, September 26, at 7:00 P.M. for the dedication of the new sports arena. (Ordinaryly) parking is allowed in the south lot. However, the construction to (widin) the auditorium has made this area dangerous and not easily (navigeable,) so it is (permissable) to park on the hockey field. If needed, we will (desigate) another area for parking.

(Regretfuly) there has been some confusion about the dates of the dances and Super Saturdays. I will (intensfy) my efforts to (clarefy) the schedule.

Miscellaneous Notes

The administration has asked me to pass on some reminders. Please be (cautous) in the construction area. It should be (fuly) safe by the end of next week. Also, parents who possess a talent for (accuricy) with numbers are needed to tally magazine drive receipts. Please call the school to volunteer.

I look forward to serving the freshman class.

Sincerely,
Anna Smith
Freshman Class President

1. reliably
2. deepen
3. gratitude
4. delicious
5. division
6. knowingly
7. automatically

8. possession
9. congregate
10. Ordinarily
11. widen
12. navigable
13. permissible
14. designate

15. Regretfully
16. intensify
17. clarify
18. cautious
19. fully
20. accuracy

Spelling Power

Lesson 25: Compound Words

Word Bank

blue gray	brother-in-law	drive-in	forty-five	long-lived
sacklike	self-conscious	tape recording	warehouse	well-done

Key Concepts

A compound word—a word that consists of two or more words that are combined to make a new word—can be a noun or an adjective. There are three types of compound words. A solid compound is a combination of words spelled as one word. An open compound is a combination of words that forms a single concept but is spelled as two or more words without a hyphen. A hyphenated compound is a combination of words joined by one or more hyphens. The following are a few of the guidelines for spelling compound words. When in doubt about the proper spelling of a compound word, consult your dictionary.

1. Hyphenate compound nouns that end with *in*, as in *drive-in*.

2. Hyphenate numbers from twenty-one to ninety-nine, as in *forty-five*.

3. Hyphenate compound adjectives such as *well-done* and *long-lived* when they precede a noun, but leave them open if they follow a noun. For example, write a *"well-done* performance," but "a performance that was well done." If the meaning of an open compound that follows a noun is unclear, hyphenate it.

4. Hyphenate most compound adjectives that begin with *all, half,* or *self,* as in *self-conscious*.

5. Hyphenate compound words that indicate family relationships by the words *great* and *in-law,* as in *brother-in-law.* Compound words with *grand* are closed, as in *grandfather.*

6. Compound words formed with the suffix *-like* are usually closed, as in *sacklike.*

7. Compound nouns made up of a noun + a gerund (the *-ing* form of a verb) can be open or closed, as in *tape recording* and *dressmaking.*

7. Most compounds formed with *house* and *ache* are closed, as in *warehouse* and *headache.*

8. Compounds for colors that indicate blends are usually left open, as in *blue gray*.

Spelling Practice

Draw a line through the word or phrase in each set that is spelled incorrectly. Then write the word or phrase correctly on the line provided.

1. ~~blue gray uniform~~   blue gray uniform   _blue gray uniform_

2. ~~drive in movie~~   drive-in movie   _drive-in movie_

3. warehouse   ~~ware house~~   _warehouse_

4. tape recording   ~~tape-recording~~   _tape recording_

5. forty-five musicians   ~~forty five musicians~~   _forty-five musicians_

6. ~~sack-like dress~~   sacklike dress   _sacklike dress_

LESSON 25 continued

7. ~~long-lived family~~	long-lived family	long-lived family
8. ~~well-done steak~~	well-done steak	well-done steak
9. brother-in-law	~~brother-in-law~~	brother-in-law
10. ~~self-conscious child~~	self-conscious child	self-conscious child

Spelling in Context

In each sentence below, find the misspelled word and circle it. Then write its correct spelling.

1. The businesswoman was (self conscious) when she spoke in public.   self-conscious

2. Melanie informed him that the (ware-house) was full.   warehouse

3. Adam preferred eating (well done) hamburgers.   well-done

4. William has (forty five) great-grandchildren.   forty-five

5. Stella had trouble finding her keys in her (sack-like) purse.   sacklike

Proofreading Practice

Read the paragraph below. Find the five misspelled words and circle them. Then write the correct spellings of the words on the lines below the paragraph.

It had been a long time since Lynn had been to the (drive in) The (tape-recording) from the old movie brought back those memories as if it were yesterday. She remembered her dad and his sister and (brother in law) piling the children into the (blue-gray) station wagon and her cousins spilling the popcorn they had brought from home. Lynn sighed as she recalled many of her family's good times. She was glad she had such (long lived) memories.

1. drive-in

2. tape recording

3. brother-in-law

4. blue gray

5. long-lived

Spelling Application

Listed below are five additional words that fit the patterns you have learned. Choose the correct word to answer each question and write the word on the line provided.

cookbook   decision making   follow-up   headache   self-confident

1. Which words are solid compounds?   cookbook   headache

2. Which word is an open compound?   decision making

3. Which words are hyphenated compounds?   follow-up   self-confident

Spelling Power

Lesson 26: The Word Roots *cede/ceed/ces* and *cept/ceive*

Word Bank

acceptable	concession	exceed	exceptional	preceding
procedure	procession	receptionist	receivable	recess

Key Concepts

There are many common word roots that contain the basic meanings of words. The word root *cede/ceed/ces* means "go." The word root *cept/ceive* means "take." Keep the following guidelines in mind when spelling words with these word roots.

1. The word root *cede* and its variant *ceed* can be difficult to spell because they are both pronounced the same way. Remember that the *ceed* spelling is used in only a few words, such as *exceed, succeed,* and *proceed.*

2. Drop the final *e* in *cede* when adding a suffix that begins with a vowel. For example, *precede* becomes *preceding.*

3. The *ces* word root variant appears in many nouns and adjectives, as in *concession, procession,* and *recess.*

4. The word root *cept/ceive* follows prefixes, as in *acceptable, exceptional,* and *receive.* When adding a suffix that begins with a vowel to a *ceive* word, drop the final *e,* as in *receivable.*

5. The *ceive* word root changes to *cept* before *ion.* For example, *receive* becomes *receptionist.*

Spelling Practice

Draw a line through the word in each set that is spelled incorrectly. Then write the word correctly on the line provided.

1. ~~procesion~~
   receivable
   procession

2. concession
   ~~excede~~
   exceed

3. recess
   ~~proceedure~~
   procedure

4. ~~receiveable~~
   exceptional
   receivable

5. ~~concesion~~
   receptionist
   concession

6. ~~reces~~
   procession
   recess

7. exceed
   ~~preceeding~~
   preceding

8. ~~acceptible~~
   procedure
   acceptable

9. preceding
   ~~recepionist~~
   receptionist

10. ~~exeptional~~
    acceptable
    exceptional

LESSON 26 continued

Spelling in Context

Complete each sentence below with the correct word from the Word Bank.

1. The doctor said that the __procedure__ would take only ten minutes.

2. If you __exceed__ the time allotted, you will be penalized.

3. The student did not want to play during __recess__, but the teacher encouraged him to take a break from schoolwork.

4. The __concession__ stand sold popcorn and ice cream.

5. The shipping clerk said that the order would be __receivable__ on Tuesday.

Proofreading Practice

Read the paragraph below. Find the five misspelled words and circle them. Then write the correct spellings of the words on the lines below the paragraph.

It was an (excepptional) day for the law firm. The (procesion) of children marched past the board members and their (recepttionist) The lawyers smiled, knowing that the playground they had built was a beginning—a better than (acceptible) solution to the problems they had been addressing in the (preceeding) months.

1. __exceptional__   3. __receptionist__   5. __preceding__

2. __procession__   4. __acceptable__

Spelling Application

Listed below are ten additional words that fit the patterns you have learned. Below the list are scrambled forms of the words. Unscramble each word and write it correctly on the line provided.

accept	access	concede	conceive	deceptive
excessive	intercede	proceeding	recede	succession

1. sescxveei __excessive__   6. ccpate __accept__

2. ssscceiuon __succession__   7. eeerdc __recede__

3. eeedvicpt __deceptive__   8. ieeoccnv __conceive__

4. gneeidrpoc __proceeding__   9. eeeintcdr __intercede__

5. ssccea __access__   10. cceedon __concede__

Spelling Power

Lesson 27: Words Borrowed from Other Languages

Word Bank

aloha	boutique	chaise longue	fiancée	hacienda
khaki	Mardi Gras	noel	tortilla	villa

Key Concepts

This lesson focuses on words that were borrowed from other languages and have become part of the English language. Few recognizable patterns apply to the spelling of these words. However, knowing their origins can help you remember how to spell them. If a foreign word has become part of the English language, you will find it in a dictionary with its origin indicated. Try to visualize these words as you study their spelling.

1. Many French words end in silent letters, including *boutique,* "a small, fashionable shop" and *chaise longue,* "a long reclining chair." Other words with French origins include *Mardi Gras,* "Fat Tuesday"; *noel,* "a Christmas carol"; and *fiancée,* "a woman engaged to be married." The accent mark over the *e* indicates that it is pronounced \ā\.

2. Some words come from the Spanish language. These words commonly end with the letter *a,* as in *hacienda,* "a large estate," and *tortilla,* "round, flat, unleavened bread."

3. Words from other languages include *villa,* "a country estate" in Italian; *aloha,* "hello" or "goodbye" in Hawaiian; and *khaki,* "a light yellowish brown" in Hindi.

Spelling Practice

Draw a line through the word in each set that is spelled incorrectly. Then write the word correctly.

1. ~~chais lounge~~   chaise longue
   chaise longue

2. ~~noele~~   noel
   noel

3. villa   ~~vila~~
   villa

4. ~~alowha~~   aloha
   aloha

5. tortilla   ~~torteya~~
   tortilla

6. ~~fianca~~   fiancée
   fiancée

7. khaki   ~~kacki~~
   khaki

8. ~~Marde Gra~~   Mardi Gras
   Mardi Gras

9. ~~bouteck~~   boutique
   boutique

10. ~~haceyenda~~   hacienda
    hacienda

Spelling in Context

Complete each sentence below with the correct word from the Word Bank.

1. On Christmas Eve, the church choir sang Monique's favorite ___noel___.

2. When they arrived in Hawaii, they were greeted by cries of "___aloha___."

LESSON 27 continued

3. Ella wore a black suit with a __khaki_____ scarf that matched her shoes.

4. Whenever Brad ate at the Mexican restaurant, he ordered __tortilla_____ chips and salsa.

5. One of Teresa's favorite places to shop was at the local __boutique_____.

Proofreading Practice

Read the paragraph below. Find the five misspelled words and circle them. Then write the correct spellings of the words on the lines below the paragraph.

Ray surveyed the land around him. His (fiance) called the estate a (vila) but he preferred to call it a (hacianda). It didn't matter. It all belonged to them now. He lowered himself onto the (chaas lounge). Finally he could begin to plan their (Marde Gra) wedding.

1. __fiancée_____ **3.** __hacienda_____ **5.** __Mardi Gras_____

2. __villa_____ **4.** __chaise longue_____

Spelling Application

Listed below are ten additional foreign words that are now considered part of the English language. Read each crossword puzzle clue. Then determine which word matches the clue and write the word in the squares.

| à la mode | cabaret | bonbon | bon voyage | en route |
| llama | matinee | plaza | shampoo | solitaire |

Across

1. French word meaning "alone"
4. Spanish word meaning "public town square"
5. French phrase meaning "in fashion"
9. French word meaning "good journey"

Down

1. Hindi word meaning "hair wash"
2. Spanish word describing an animal related to a camel
3. French phrase meaning "on the way"
6. French word describing entertainment that takes place in the daytime
7. French word meaning "a special type of chocolate candy"
8. French word meaning "nightclub"

Spelling Power

Lesson 28: Antonyms

Word Bank

adaptable / rigid   exquisite / hideous   integrate / segregate   optimistic / pessimistic   prevent / encourage

Key Concepts

Antonyms are words that have opposite meanings. *Hot* and *cold* are antonyms. Antonyms may be verbs, nouns, or adjectives. Some antonyms are formed by adding a negative prefix, such as *dis-, in-,* or *non-,* to a word root. You can define new words if you know that the new word is the antonym of a word you already know. For example, if you know the meaning of *hideous,* you can guess the meaning of its antonym, *exquisite.* You can also use context clues to determine the meaning of antonyms. Try to visualize these words as you study their spelling.

1. *Adaptable* means "able to change easily with new circumstances." Its antonym is *inflexible* or *rigid.*
2. *Optimistic* means "having an inclination to think positively," whereas *pessimistic* means "having an inclination to think negatively."
3. *Exquisite* means "pleasing through beauty." Its antonym is *hideous,* which means "exceedingly ugly."
4. To *prevent* something means "to keep something from happening"; to *encourage* means "to stimulate something."
5. To *integrate* is "to unite with something else," whereas to *segregate* is "to separate or set apart from others."

Spelling Practice

In each set below, circle the word whose meaning is opposite the meaning of the capitalized word. Then write the word on the line provided.

1. RIGID   (adaptable)   hideous   adaptable
2. SEGREGATE   pessimistic   (integrate)   integrate
3. ADAPTABLE   prevent   (rigid)   rigid
4. PREVENT   (encourage)   exquisite   encourage
5. OPTIMISTIC   segregate   (pessimistic)   pessimistic
6. INTEGRATE   (segregate)   adaptable   segregate
7. HIDEOUS   (exquisite)   encourage   exquisite
8. PESSIMISTIC   integrate   (optimistic)   optimistic
9. ENCOURAGE   (prevent)   rigid   prevent
10. EXQUISITE   optimistic   (hideous)   hideous

LESSON 28 continued

Spelling in Context

Decide which word from the Word Bank is defined in each phrase below. Then write the word.

1. to stimulate __encourage__
2. to separate __segregate__
3. able to change easily with new circumstances __adaptable__
4. always thinking positively __optimistic__
5. to unite with something else __integrate__

Proofreading Practice

Read the paragraph below. Find the five misspelled words and circle them. Then write the correct spellings of the words on the lines below the paragraph.

Camryn's twin was always so riged—so pesimistic. Why shouldn't they buy those exquisit dresses for the prom? Camryn thought that the evening would be hideus if she had to wear last year's dress, the thought of which would pravent her from going to the prom.

1. __rigid__
2. __pessimistic__
3. __exquisite__
4. __hideous__
5. __prevent__

Spelling Application

Listed below are five additional pairs of words that are antonyms. Find them in the word maze and circle them. Then write the pairs of antonyms on the lines provided. Word pairs may be listed in any order.

casual / formal   freeze / antifreeze   cower / strut   regard / disregard   capable / incapable

```
c o w e r l s o d s h b a
s e s z u r m n i l g e n
j g g x c e i o s m n j t
f o u l a g r m r e m o i
i n c a p a b l e n k l f
s q a w a r h w g s e s r
t e s e b d s f a v l d e
r i u j l t f o r m a l e
u p a e e t i m d n s n z
t g l k i h f r e e z e e
```

1. __antifreeze__ and __freeze__
2. __cower__ and __strut__
3. __incapable__ and __capable__
4. __formal__ and __casual__
5. __regard__ and __disregard__

Spelling Power

Unit 7 Review

Lessons 25–28

In each sentence below, find the misspelled word and circle it. Then write the word correctly.

1. In public speaking class, students learn how to overcome feeling (self concious.)   self-conscious

2. The (tortila) is a type of bread that can be stuffed, rolled, or eaten flat.   tortilla

3. As the tour bus rolled around the curve, the large stone (vila) came into view.   villa

4. A (hacianda) is usually made of clay bricks covered with white plaster.   hacienda

5. He bought his (feancee) a very expensive engagement ring.   fiancée

6. To illustrate the lesson, the teacher decided to (segreggate) the students by eye color.   segregate

7. As a (concesion) to the children, Fred let them watch cartoons.   concession

8. The taxi driver told his customer it would take (fortyfive) minutes to get to the airport.   forty-five

9. The most popular uniform used in desert warfare is (khacki) in color.   khaki

10. Follow directions for the (preceeding) exercise.   preceding

Read each statement below. Then on the lines provided, write the word, correcting any misspelling. If the statement is incorrect, rewrite it to make a true statement.

11. Compound color words such as *blue gray* need no hyphen.   blue gray

12. *Tape recording* is an example of an open compound word.   Tape recording

13. *Sack-like* is an example of a hyphenated compound word.   Sacklike

    incorrect; Close most compound words formed with the suffix *-like*.

14. *Brotherinlaw* is an example of a closed compound word.   Brother-in-law

    incorrect; Hyphenate compound words that show family relationships with the word *in-law*.

15. *Recess* includes the word root *ces*.   recess

Draw a line through the word in each set that is spelled incorrectly. Then write the word correctly.

16. ~~chase lounge~~/optimistic   chaise longue   19. ~~welldone~~/tortilla   well-done

17. integrate/~~drive in~~   drive-in   20. ~~nowel~~/warehouse   noel

18. ~~Marde Gra~~/concession   Mardi Gras

Spelling Power

Proofreading Application

Lessons 25–28
Read the speech below. Find the twenty misspelled words and circle them. Then write the correct spellings of the words on the lines below the speech.

Commencement Address to Hawaii State University

Alowha graduates. I am pleased to be here today before this exeptional group. Your seemingly long lived college era has come to an end. In a moment, you will take part in a proccesion that will send you on your way to the next phase of your lives.

Don't take that walk lightly. The opportunities are plentiful for the right individual. Some will be accepteble to you. Some will excede your wildest expectations. The important thing to remember is not to be so rijid in your expectations that you pravent yourself from considering every opportunity.

Not every opportunity starts out as the right one, however. You have a choice. You can be optemistic or pesimistic. You'll find that attitude goes a long way toward helping you reach your goals. I can tell you from personal experience that I've encountered situations that at first appeared hideos, but in the end were exquisit chances to learn and grow.

Before I conclude, I'll share one story to incourage you. A young woman with a journalism degree started her career as a recepionist at wages so low that she had to work nights in a boutiqe to pay her bills. Still she was adaptible and worked hard. She even sought out extra assignments available at the company's wearhouse.

Soon she was able to intigrate writing with her receptionist and accounts recevable duties. It was a long proceedure but eventually her work was recognized and she was promoted. Ten years later, that receptionist was vice president of that same company.

If you're curious, I was that receptionist. The point of the story is to look at the potential in every situation. Don't be afraid to try new opportunities because you never know where they might lead you.

1. Aloha
2. exceptional
3. long-lived
4. procession
5. acceptable
6. exceed
7. rigid
8. prevent
9. optimistic
10. pessimistic

11. hideous
12. exquisite
13. encourage
14. receptionist
15. boutique
16. adaptable
17. warehouse
18. integrate
19. receivable
20. procedure

Spelling Power

Lesson 29: Synonyms

Word Bank

| attempt/endeavor | dwell/reside | eliminate/eradicate | falter/hesitate | rash/reckless |

Key Concepts

Synonyms are words that have similar meanings. To decide which synonym to use, keep in mind its connotation—the ideas associated with it—and the context in which it is most frequently used. Visualize these words as you study them to help you remember the correct spelling of each.

1. *Attempt* and *endeavor* both mean "to make an effort" or "an effort," but *endeavor* implies greater difficulty and exertion.
2. *Dwell* and *reside* both mean "to live as a resident." *Dwell* can also mean "to live in a given condition or state."
3. *Eliminate* and *eradicate* both mean "to get rid of," but *eradicate* implies "to remove all traces of."
4. *Falter* and *hesitate* both mean "to pause." *Falter* implies pausing because of fear, whereas *hesitate* implies pausing due to uncertainty.
5. *Rash* and *reckless* both mean "irresponsible" or "marked by a lack of caution." *Rash* implies hasty action, whereas *reckless* implies lack of concern about the consequences of an action.

Spelling Practice

In each set below, circle the word whose meaning is similar in meaning to the capitalized word. Then write the correct word on the line provided.

1. RESIDE   (dwell)   endeavor   dwell
2. ELIMINATE   falter   (eradicate)   eradicate
3. RASH   hesitate   (reckless)   reckless
4. ATTEMPT   (endeavor)   eliminate   endeavor
5. FALTER   rash   (hesitate)   hesitate
6. ENDEAVOR   (attempt)   dwell   attempt
7. RECKLESS   eradicate   (rash)   rash
8. DWELL   (reside)   falter   reside
9. ERADICATE   endeavor   (eliminate)   eliminate
10. HESITATE   (falter)   reside   falter

LESSON 29 continued

Spelling in Context

Complete each sentence below with the correct word from the Word Bank.

1. Although Emily's house was in shambles after the tornado, she continued to __dwell or reside__ there.

2. Advances in medicine have allowed doctors to __eradicate or eliminate__ certain diseases.

3. When Macey was offered the new job, she didn't __hesitate__ before accepting it.

4. Warren decided to make one more __attempt__ to ride the horse.

5. Everyone thought that Al had made a __rash or reckless__ decision when he suddenly quit his job.

Proofreading Practice

Read the paragraph below. Find the five misspelled words and circle them. Then write the correct spellings of the words on the lines below the paragraph.

Because Andrew had never played a sport before, his friends thought his decision to try out for the football team was recless. They told Andrew the coach would elimenate him immediately. However, during tryouts Andrew did not faller and was successful in his endevors to impress the coach. Andrew made the team and now he practically rezides on the football field.

1. reckless   3. falter   5. resides

2. eliminate   4. endeavors

Spelling Application

Listed below are five additional synonym pairs. Circle these words in the word maze. Then write each pair of words on the lines below.

conservative/traditional   crave/desire   entice/lure   isolate/seclude   maneuver/manipulate

```
f t h m a c s j u d k l
d r m a n e u v e r e i
s a e t a l o s i g m o
e d p o n v s x b e b
c o n s e r v a t i v e
l u r e e n h t q u a l
u l a n o i t d a r t
d u k b g e a i t y c m
e j n c h e t y c v a y
m a n i p u l a t e l k
```

1. conservative / traditional   4. isolate / seclude

2. crave / desire   5. maneuver / manipulate

3. entice / lure

Name _____ Date _____ Class _____

Lesson 30: Homonyms

Word Bank

altar / alter	capital / capitol	colonel / kernel	currant / current	stationary / stationery

Key Concepts

Homonyms are words that have the same pronunciations but different spellings and meanings. There are no patterns to follow for the spelling of homonyms. To decide which homonym to use in writing, keep in mind the meaning of each homonym and the context in which it is to be used. Try to visualize these words as you study to help you remember their correct spellings.

1. *altar:* a table or stand used in religious services
   alter: to change
2. *capital:* an uppercase letter; the city where the state or national government is located
   capitol: the building where the state legislature meets; (Capitol) the building where the U.S. Congress meets
3. *colonel:* a military rank
   kernel: a small piece
4. *currant:* a type of berry
   current: recent; continuously moving air or water
5. *stationary:* immobile; in a fixed position
   stationery: paper for writing letters

Creating memory aids can help connect a word's spelling with its meaning. For example, *stationery* spelled with an *e* refers to writing paper and envelopes. If you think *e* for envelopes, you will be able link the proper spelling with that meaning.

Spelling Practice

Draw a line thorugh the word in each set that is spelled incorrectly. Then write the word correctly.

1. a stationary bicycle	a ~~stationery~~ bicycle	stationary
2. a kernel of corn	a ~~colonel~~ of corn	kernel
3. the cathedral's ~~alter~~	the cathedral's altar	altar
4. current events	~~currant~~ events	current
5. a capital letter	a ~~capitol~~ letter	capital
6. the U.S. Capitol	the U.S. ~~Capital~~	Capitol
7. stationery for writing	~~stationary~~ for writing	stationery
8. eating a currant	eating a ~~current~~	currant
9. to alter	to ~~altar~~	alter
10. an army colonel	an army ~~kernel~~	colonel

LESSON 30 continued

Spelling in Context

In each sentence below, find the misspelled word and circle it. Then write its correct spelling on the line provided.

1. No one has wound the clock, so the hands have been (stationery) for years. _stationary_

2. She hurt her tooth on an unpopped (colonel) of popcorn. _kernel_

3. The groom was standing in front of the (alter) waiting for his bride. _altar_

4. Red (current) jam is one of my favorites. _currant_

5. Ottawa is the (capitol) of Canada. _capital_

Proofreading Practice

Read the paragraph below. Find the five misspelled words and circle them. Then write the correct spellings of the words on the lines below the paragraph.

After looking in several drawers, Dana found the hotel (stationary) and sat down to compose a note. She apologized to the (kernel) and explained that she could not meet him at the (Capital) the following morning as she had planned. Her (currant) situation had changed, and Dana had to (altar) her plans.

1. _stationery_   3. _Capitol_   5. _alter_

2. _colonel_   4. _current_

Spelling Application

Listed below are five additional pairs of homonyms. Read each crossword puzzle clue. Then determine which word matches the clue and write the word in the squares provided.

brows / browse   clause / claws   dual / duel   liar / lyre   miner / minor

Across

4. a distinct item in a formal document
7. a person who digs for coal
8. a person who does not tell the truth
9. to look around in a shop
10. the sharp, slender, and curved nails on an animal's toes

Down

1. a competition to settle a dispute
2. of little importance
3. having two components
5. a small harp
6. hair above the eyes

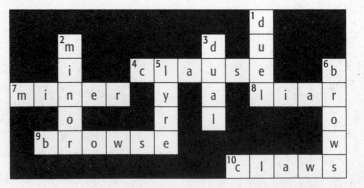

Spelling Power

Spelling Power

Lesson 31: Words Often Confused

Word Bank

adjoin / adjourn   affect / effect   decent / descent   moral / morale   profit / prophet

Key Concepts

There are many words in the English language that can be easily confused. The confusion occurs because the words have similar spellings or pronunciations or because they are homonyms. There are no spelling patterns to follow for these words. Commit the following word pairs to memory. Try to visualize these words as you study to help you remember their correct spellings.

1. *adjoin:* to be placed next to
   adjourn: to postpone until a later time or indefinitely
2. *affect:* to influence
   effect: the result
3. *decent:* proper; satisfactory
   descent: fall; the process of coming down

4. *moral:* lesson; ethical
   morale: attitude toward, or mood regarding, a task or situation
5. *profit:* to gain earnings; income
   prophet: one who predicts the future

Spelling Practice

In each set below, circle the word whose meaning is close to the meaning of the capitalized word. Then write the circled word on the line.

1. RESULT   affect   (effect)   effect
2. ETHICAL   (moral)   morale   moral
3. POSTPONE   adjoin   (adjourn)   adjourn
4. VISIONARY   profit   (prophet)   prophet
5. INFLUENCE   (affect)   effect   affect
6. MOOD   moral   (morale)   morale
7. DROP   decent   (descent)   descent
8. EARN   (profit)   prophet   profit
9. ATTACH   (adjoin)   adjourn   adjoin
10. SATISFACTORY   (decent)   descent   decent

LESSON 31 continued

Spelling in Context

Complete each sentence with the correct word from the Word Bank.

1. The _____moral_____ of the fable was not to be deceived by flattery.

2. Despite our lack of proper equipment, we made the _____descent_____ down the side of the mountain.

3. The _____prophet_____ predicted world peace during our lifetimes.

4. Dan worried about whether the road construction would _____affect_____ his drive to work.

5. Our rooms at the hotel _____adjoin_____ so we should be able to find each other easily.

Proofreading Practice

Read the paragraph below. Find the five misspelled words and circle them. Then write the correct spellings of the words on the lines below the paragraph.

At our company's annual meeting, the head of sales reported that moral was high and that we had earned a descent prophet as a result of the changes made last year. The president said that he hoped the good news would have a positive affect and he moved to adjoin the meeting.

1. _____morale_____   3. _____profit_____   5. _____adjourn_____

2. _____decent_____   4. _____effect_____

Spelling Application

Listed below are five additional pairs of words that are easily confused. Read each crossword puzzle clue. Then determine which word matches the clue and write it in the squares provided.

adapt / adopt   corps / corpse   detract / distract   forceful / forcible   legislator / legislature

Across

2. person who makes laws
3. involving the use of force
4. draw attention from
5. take away from
6. to change or adjust
7. to choose as one's own
8. a dead body

Down

1. group of people
2. group of lawmakers
3. strong, powerful

Spelling Power

Lesson 32: Words Often Misspelled

Word Bank

application	appropriate	coincidence	cylinder	existence
fatigue	monitor	nuclear	specifically	technical

Key Concepts

Some words in the English language are especially difficult to spell. This lesson focuses on a small group of commonly mis-spelled words. They may contain trouble spots such as double consonants or silent letters. As you become aware of your spelling trouble spots, you can create your own list of words to commit to memory. Try to visualize these words as you study to help you remember their correct spellings.

1. Words ending in -ence and -ance are often misspelled because the endings sound the same, as in *coincidence, existence,* and *tolerance.*

2. Words ending in -ly and -ally are confused because the endings sound the same, as in *specifically* and *utterly.*

3. Some words, such as *application* and *appropriate,* have double consonants that are often mistakenly spelled as a single consonant.

4. Some words have letters that are not pronounced. For example, in *fatigue,* the *u* and the *e* are silent.

5. The *er, or,* and *ar* endings may be confused because all are pronounced with a schwa (\ə\) before the *r,* as in *cylinder, monitor,* and *nuclear.*

6. The -al, -lc, and -el endings may also be confused because they are all pronounced with the \ə\ sound, as in *horrible, label,* and *technical.*

Spelling Practice

Draw a line thorough the word in each set that is spelled incorrectly. Then write the word correctly on the line provided.

1. ~~nucleor~~   nuclear
   _nuclear_____

2. ~~coincidance~~   coincidence
   _coincidence_____

3. fatigue   ~~fatige~~
   _fatigue_____

4. ~~moniter~~   monitor
   _monitor_____

5. ~~specificly~~   specifically
   _specifically_____

6. technical   ~~technicol~~
   _technical_____

7. cylinder   ~~cylindar~~
   _cylinder_____

8. application   ~~aplication~~
   _application_____

9. appropriate   ~~apropriate~~
   _appropriate_____

10. existence   ~~existance~~
    _existence_____

LESSON 32 continued

Spelling in Context

Decide which word from the Word Bank is described in each phrase below. Then write the word on the line provided.

1. when events randomly happen at the same time

2. a tube-shaped object

3. a type of energy

4. dealing with mechanics or science

5. life

coincidence

cylinder

nuclear

technical

existence

Proofreading Practice

Read the paragraph below. Find the five misspelled words and circle them. Then write the correct spellings of the word on the lines below the paragraph.

    Rosa rubbed her eyes and tried to fight her fatig. She had been staring at the moniter all day, trying to do her essay for her college aplication. She was having a difficult time choosing an apropriate topic. Specificly she couldn't decide whether to write about her trip to Europe or about her volunteer work.

1. fatigue

2. monitor

3. application

4. appropriate

5. Specifically

Spelling Application

Listed below are five additional words that are commonly misspelled. Find them in the word maze and circle them. Then write the words from the maze on the lines provided.

environment   exhibition   obstacle   pronunciation   versus

```
r e n v i r o n m e n t s
y v w s a u h j a m z t c
d e l c a t s b o n x x d
p r o n u n c i a t i o n
f s s d m u o a a m g a g
m u a e x h i b i t i o n
u s l g m a p d t m a s c
```

1. environment

2. exhibition

3. obstacle

4. pronunciation

5. versus

Spelling Power

Unit 8 Review

Lessons 29–32

In each sentence below, find the misspelled word and circle it. Then write its correct spelling on the line provided.

1. The (Capital) is in the center of town.   Capitol

2. The (kernel) ordered his troops to retreat.   colonel

3. The (alter) at the church was the most beautiful she had seen.   altar

4. The plane began its (decent) into the airport.   descent

5. They decided to (adjoin) the meeting at three o'clock.   adjourn

6. All I want is a (descent) night's sleep.   decent

7. The bathroom (adjourns) the bedroom upstairs.   adjoins

8. They disagreed on the (morale) of the story.   moral

9. Many of his predictions had come true, so many people considered him to be a (profit.)   prophet

10. She was no longer hungry so she put the bowl of (current) jam in the refrigerator.   currant

Draw a line through the word in each set that is spelled incorrectly. Then write the word correctly on the line provided.

11. coincidance   dwell   coincidence

12. falter   recide   reside

13. dwel   existence   dwell

14. cylinder   atempt   attempt

15. existence   faltor   falter

16. nuclear   cylindar   cylinder

17. nucleir   attempt   nuclear

18. coincidence   existance   existence

19. rash   rekless   reckless

20. rasch   reckless   rash

Spelling Power

Proofreading Application

Lessons 29–32
Read the business letter below. Find the twenty misspelled words and circle them. Then write the correct spellings of the words on the lines below the letter.

June 15, 2000

Dear Customer:

   We are writing to inform you of our new products for this season. We hope you will find them suitable for your currant needs.

• The E-Z Stationery Bike: This bicycle makes working out a breeze. Whether the goal of your endeavers is to lose a few pounds or just to get in shape, this bike is sure to have an affect. It will altar the way you look and boost your moral in just a few short months.

• The Big Byte Computer and Moniter: This computer has enough hard drive space to accommodate all of your programs, whether you use your system for pleasure or prophet. It doesn't require a lot of capitol either—just a small monthly payment.

• Corn Scrub: One aplication of our new oatmeal, honey, and corn-colonel scrub will effect your skin in marvelous ways.

• Fatige Relief: This specially formulated pillow will eradecate tension and strain in your neck. If you sleep on this pillow, you are guaranteed a good night's rest.

   We want to elliminate any difficulty you may have. If at any time you have technicle problems specificly related to our products or if you would like additional information, please do not hesetate to contact us. You will find the apropriate addresses on our stationary.

   Thank you again for your business. We look forward to serving you in the future.

Sincerely,
Bob Smith
Products U.S.A.

1. current
2. Stationary
3. endeavors
4. effect
5. alter
6. morale
7. Monitor
8. profit
9. capital
10. application

11. kernel
12. affect
13. Fatigue
14. eradicate
15. eliminate
16. technical
17. specifically
18. hesitate
19. appropriate
20. stationery

Name _____ Date _____ Class _____

Oral Quizzes

Lesson 1

1. The class was **wholly** in favor of donating the proceeds of the bake sale and car wash to charity.
2. The members of the **committee** met to discuss possible themes for the spring dance.
3. The **omission** of my name from the invitation list was an oversight that was easily corrected.
4. The director of the play announced that Marie would take the role of the **villain.**
5. Kyle's happy reaction to the news was the **opposite** of what I had expected.
6. The **questionnaire** was designed to find out testers' reactions to the new product.
7. Her parents were worried that the attention Regina received for rescuing the dog from the river would **embarrass** her.
8. The main highway and the rural road are **parallel** to each other, but the back road has less traffic.
9. In **accordance** with the agreement she made with her parents, Sandra would lose privileges if she missed her curfew.
10. As a small child, Tyler had a slight tendency to **exaggerate** accounts of his adventures.
11. After the farmer developed a way to **irrigate** the north field, his wheat harvests improved greatly.
12. The **hurricane** was reported to be approaching the coast quickly.
13. The **bulletin** issued from the White House reported that the President was in good health.
14. The **opportunity** to study abroad filled Eve with excitement as well as anxiety.
15. Anna rearranged her schedule so that she did not **disappoint** her family by missing the reunion.

Lesson 2

1. The uppermost **limb** of the tree had to be removed because it was caught on the power lines.
2. Please **fasten** the helium balloons securely to the tent entrance so that they do not float away.
3. During our tour of the haunted house, we were treated to **ghastly** shrieks from dark figures in the corner.
4. In the museum, a visitor can see the illustrated copies of each **psalm.**
5. Because of the temperate climate in the South, the season of **autumn** is recognized only by an increase in rainfall.
6. The dog will **gnaw** at the bone until every scrap of meat has disappeared.
7. "Bundle up so that you don't get **pneumonia,**" shouted the mother to the children playing in the snow.
8. When the truck tilted on the incline of the hill, its **freight** of marbles began to roll all over the road.
9. The physical therapist will **knead** the back muscles of the patient.
10. The new owners transformed the **wretched** house into a comfortable and cheerful home.
11. Please look **through** your books carefully before turning them in.
12. Steve dressed as a **ghost** at the costume party.
13. The plumber used his **wrench** to fix the leaky pipe.
14. The **knowledge** that she would soon be moving made each day in her old house more special.
15. **Psychology** is the science of the study of the human mind.

ORAL QUIZZES continued

Lesson 3

1. Although Paula thought she had followed the **recipe** exactly, she later realized that she had omitted the vanilla.

2. Steve made a futile attempt to **disguise** the odor of burnt cheese by spraying air freshener in the kitchen.

3. Many people spend a great deal of time tracing their **ancestry** in hope of finding a famous relative.

4. As you grow older, you learn to **censor** the thoughts and emotions that you share with others.

5. The school began a fund-raising campaign to earn money for a new **gymnasium** and sports complex.

6. Although getting a low grade seemed like a **tragedy,** it motivated her to work harder and accomplish more in the class than she would have otherwise.

7. An unexpected **circumstance** prevented me from attending the final basketball game.

8. The couple tried to **recapture** the romantic feelings they had for each other when they first met.

9. Labeling her a **genius** on the basis of one test score seems premature.

10. After Ben's tenth question in five minutes, his brother exclaimed impatiently, "Don't **plague** me!"

11. Sondra's **imaginary** pet disappeared when her parents gave her a real puppy for her birthday.

12. The doctor rejoiced that the treatment she had developed led to **success** in conquering the disease.

13. The mother suggested to her son that it might be **necessary** for him to study before the final exam.

14. We decided to ride our tandem **bicycle** in the park.

15. When we heard that the twins were coming for Thanksgiving, we removed all **fragile** objects from the shelves and locked the china cabinet.

Lesson 4

1. It was difficult for Samantha to **rouse** herself after a long study session.

2. Two hours after we were due to arrive at our destination, we realized that we must have missed the **guidepost.**

3. The antique collector pounced on the **bureau** at the garage sale and bought it immediately.

4. Vinnie set aside time for a **thorough** proofreading of his research paper before he handed it in to be graded.

5. In the book, the **chieftain** had both good and bad qualities.

6. The pressure **gauge** indicated that there was not enough air in the two front tires.

7. Although I see Devon at work every day, I consider her to be just an **acquaintance.**

8. The baying of the wolves was thrilling at first, but after several hours, the sound became a **nuisance.**

9. The **peasant** trudged wearily behind the plow.

10. Her **haughty** attitude concealed her shyness and fear at being in a new school.

11. Norman informed his neighbor that the **boundary** between their houses was the sprawling oak tree.

12. The **captain** of the team is responsible for setting standards of good sportsmanship.

13. Some European explorers mistakenly referred to the native peoples they met as **heathen.**

14. Ursula tied the laces on her skate so that they were **taut** around her ankle.

15. After climbing steadily for three weeks, my grade in geometry class reached a **plateau.**

ORAL QUIZZES continued

Lesson 5

1. We took an **aerial** tram to the top of the mountain.
2. One **aisle** of the airplane cabin seems to be much wider than the other.
3. The geometry teacher drew a **trapezoid** on the board.
4. After a lengthy custody battle, the court appointed him the child's **guardian.**
5. Nancy bought a **souvenir** from the museum gift shop for her brother.
6. Everyone was nervous at the last **rehearsal** before opening night.
7. The **soybean** crop is ready to be harvested.
8. We thought the painting was a mass-produced copy of the original, but the art dealer assured us that it was **authentic.**
9. The girls look so much alike; they are **undoubtedly** related.
10. Jack and Dana had a good time watching the **uproarious** movie.
11. Posters of famous baseball players on every wall in his bedroom indicate that he is a **devout** fan.
12. The coach hoped to **empower** her field hockey players to do their best.
13. The **numerator** is the number above the line in a fraction.
14. The **outbound** train will leave in twenty minutes.
15. A substitute was called when the **regular** teacher was ill.

Lesson 6

1. Many stores have procedures for identifying **counterfeit** money.
2. The paint on the **ceiling** of the abandoned house was peeling.
3. Sarah's mother always reminded her that sincere effort would enable her to **achieve** her goals.
4. She was angry that Larry had tried to **deceive** her.
5. You may have **either** pizza or a sandwich for lunch.
6. The artist draws **weird** creatures in his comic strip.
7. My **niece** and my nephew are active in school sports.
8. A **vein** carries blood to the heart.
9. Before Mandy brought the package to the post office, she used a scale to **weigh** it.
10. After the funeral, the family needed time to **grieve.**
11. Telling the truth gave Cathy a clear **conscience.**
12. Because the tennis player's partner did not appear, they were forced to **forfeit** the doubles match.
13. We spent the afternoon fishing from the **pier.**
14. Pamela prepared to **receive** her dinner guests promptly at five.
15. The rich soil should **yield** a good crop.

ORAL QUIZZES continued

Lesson 7

1. Ryan holds a **controlling** interest in the company.
2. The rules **governing** the wrestling competition are quite strict.
3. Managers for each region attended the sales **conference.**
4. No visitors to the park can gain **admittance** after sunset.
5. The spoiled dog **begged** for another treat from his owner.
6. Choir members **visited** residents of the nursing home before the concert.
7. Loud talking is not **permitted** in the library.
8. Carolyn used sunscreen so the sun wouldn't **redden** her skin.
9. Babies are **totally** dependent on their parents.
10. Junkyard dogs are known for **meanness.**
11. The waitress **accidentally** dropped the heavy tray on the ceramic floor.
12. Flowers are **beginning** to bloom in the garden.
13. For a change of scenery, we **occasionally** take a different route home.
14. The doctor **referred** his patient to a specialist.
15. Juanita **transferred** money from her savings account to her checking account.

Lesson 8

1. Roger received a letter of **acknowledgment** for his generous donation.
2. The builder gave us a contract **guaranteeing** that the work would be completed in one month.
3. The ranchers spent the day **shoeing** many horses.
4. Marla was sure that changing jobs would be an **advantageous** move.
5. Despite our objections to his busy schedule, Thomas assured us that his heavy workload was **manageable.**
6. Planting more flowers made a **noticeable** improvement in the garden.
7. Janet felt **virtuous** for working so hard at the fund drive.
8. Todd was interested in a career in law **enforcement.**
9. Marilyn is **truly** dedicated to the needs of the refugee community.
10. The **scarcity** of drinking water was brought about by the long drought.
11. I learned how to make a floral **arrangement** in the workshop.
12. The weather report warned of **changeable** temperatures.
13. Matt used good **judgment** in making his decision.
14. The trail leads into the mountains **lying** ahead of us.
15. She **sincerely** thanked the committee for giving her the award.

ORAL QUIZZES continued

Lesson 9

1. Telling his secret is a **betrayal** of the promise you made to your friend.
2. Erin's room was such a mess that she could not see where she **laid** her homework.
3. Shayna's angry posture and stare of **defiance** showed she was not yet ready to talk calmly.
4. Her attentive gaze showed Amy's **readiness** to tackle the project.
5. Some topics are too **controversial** to discuss on a first date.
6. Audrey received a call from the airport **verifying** that the flight was on time.
7. Michael was **overjoyed** to discover that he had been accepted by Princeton University.
8. I am **envious** of your short walk to school because it allows you to sleep longer.
9. The train chugged **steadily** up the long, steep hill.
10. Your failure to do the assignment **implies** that you do not care about your grade.
11. My **employer** is not very understanding.
12. Butch tore a New York City telephone book in half to show his **manliness.**
13. Great rulers are also **merciful** ones.
14. David **shinnied** up the great oak tree.
15. The victory was instrumental in **unifying** the soccer team.

Lesson 10

1. **Fezes** were worn at all important ceremonies.
2. There are two **approaches** to the island from the mainland.
3. The baker prepared one hundred **loaves** of bread each day.
4. You have three **guesses** to solve the puzzle.
5. The baby always gets several **splashes** of milk on his shirt.
6. The **indexes** are the best place to look for information on your topic.
7. His **cuffs** were neatly pressed, although his collar was not.
8. Her silk **scarves** were the most popular item at the craft show.
9. I always use at least two **handkerchiefs** when watching sad movies.
10. I always confuse **wolves** with coyotes.
11. My political **beliefs** have changed over time.
12. The school parking lot was filled with **buses** at midafternoon.
13. The night sky was lit with **flashes** of lightning.
14. Keep young children away from **knives,** or there is likely to be an accident.
15. **Peaches** are my favorite summertime fruit.

ORAL QUIZZES continued

Lesson 11

1. To many fans, Michael Jordan is one of the greatest sports **heroes** of all time.

2. When the power goes out, battery-powered **radios** are a good source for news.

3. The game had four **categories** of questions.

4. There were many travel **agencies** located within a few blocks of the hotel.

5. The distinctive **tattoos** on the fugitive's arm made it impossible for him to hide his identity.

6. Phil collected **pianos** and had one that played by itself.

7. The silk bedspread was one of her more extravagant **buys.**

8. Megan got a new pair of **skis** for her birthday.

9. The Mexican feast included **tacos** and rice with refried beans.

10. It seemed that all Steven did at work was write **memos.**

11. Several **companies** were at the job fair to look for new employees.

12. The **displays** at the science fair were impressive.

13. Because of the **echoes,** a hundred people seemed to be in the canyon.

14. The freshly scrubbed **patios** in the development seemed to shine on the day of the block party.

15. They grew **tomatoes** in their garden every summer.

Lesson 12

1. The job requires a person who remains calm during **crises.**

2. Our high school has a competitive **athletics** program.

3. **Oxen** are large beasts often used for farm work.

4. **Children** seem to enjoy life's simplest pleasures.

5. The letter went out to all of the **alumni** of the school.

6. Lauren knew she would need more **data** to complete the assignment.

7. **Salmon** swim upstream to mate and then they die.

8. The university was huge; it had a dozen **campuses.**

9. All my favorite television **series** are in reruns now.

10. There are no **minimums** required in order to qualify for the discount.

11. Although you cannot see **bacteria,** they are present.

12. The **fruit** was not ripe enough to eat, so we had to wait a few days.

13. The tree trunk was covered in **fungi.**

14. There are more pluses than **minuses** to finishing school.

15. Some men claim that they will never understand **women.**

ORAL QUIZZES continued

Lesson 13

1. You **needn't** criticize me so much when you have never changed a tire before, either.

2. We **might've** been able to buy the puppy if we had arrived before the store closed.

3. **Let's** go to the nursing home and ask if they need volunteers.

4. **He'd** better find a summer job soon.

5. **We're** the only family on our street with statues of pink flamingos on the lawn.

6. It **doesn't** look as if the sun is going to come out today.

7. I know we **should've** called first, but we didn't think that you would mind unexpected guests.

8. Next week **I'll** be in charge of opening the store early every day.

9. **It's** difficult to decide who most deserves first prize.

10. I think that **they're** on vacation because their newspapers are piling up on the doorstep.

11. Because Philip is afraid of blood, I thought that **he'd** faint when his finger bled.

12. **We've** never considered purchasing a house.

13. **Aren't** you the least bit curious about who called?

14. **Who's** your favorite athlete?

15. After witnessing your record-breaking long jump, I am confident that **you're** going to be chosen for the track and field team.

Lesson 14

1. The Roman Catholic Church sets aside November 2 as **All Souls' Day.**

2. **Father's Day** can be lonely for fathers whose children live far away.

3. This **household's** main problem is that there are no rules.

4. The **children's** bicycles are all parked in our driveway.

5. The **bosses'** desks are grouped together so they don't have to relocate when they want to have a meeting.

6. The **senators'** hotel rooms were destroyed in a fire, so they all had to make new reservations.

7. I love all of **Charles Dickens's** novels, but *A Tale of Two Cities* is my favorite.

8. My grandmother assured me that her set of china will be **ours** someday.

9. A **public figure's** responsibility is to act as a role model for all citizens.

10. The **G.I.'s** backpack served as a pillow when he was camping in the woods.

11. The **businesswomen's** lunch was canceled due to bad weather.

12. The **defendant's** posture was so terrible that he looked defeated even before the trial began.

13. The **duchess's** daughter was spoiled by a lifetime of luxury.

14. The **mourners'** umbrellas were blown inside out by the wind.

15. Her **sister-in-law's** loudly expressed opinions always embarrassed Mary.

ORAL QUIZZES continued

Lesson 15

1. Many residents were upset by the **demolition** of the old courthouse.
2. The children were **cooperative** during story time because they enjoyed the dramatic way I read to them.
3. Although we resented the **intrusion,** we tried to remain polite when we spoke to telemarketers.
4. In **biology** we studied the classification system for plants and animals.
5. The first thing that struck me about her apartment was its general **dinginess.**
6. The chef's rich food was tasty, but difficult to **digest.**
7. Trying to exchange a gift can be a **hassle** in some stores.
8. Before money was used as **currency,** most nations relied on the barter system.
9. The candidates intensified their campaign as the **election** drew near.
10. When Seth's departmental supervisors purchased the new computer system, they also bought new **software.**
11. At the fabric store, I picked up a **bobbin** of thread and some buttons.
12. We decided to **boycott** the company because of its poor record on environmental issues.
13. His **curiosity** nudged him closer to the haunted house.
14. The **accounting** department came under close scrutiny by the auditors.
15. Peter decided that Ina's **coyness** was not genuine.

Lesson 16

1. When I tried washing my football **jersey** with my red shorts, my jersey turned pink.
2. It is a very serious crime to **embezzle** funds.
3. She is a **restorer** of ancient art, and her workshop is in this city.
4. We formed our own **council** to decide whether pets should be permitted in the park.
5. Many people feel they are duty bound to serve as **jurors** in a court of law.
6. The poet compared the tree to a **pillar** in a temple.
7. I find a good workout **infinitely** satisfying.
8. When we were in Arizona, we watched Native Americans perform **tribal** dances.
9. The mixing of **sulfur** from industrial pollution with water in the atmosphere often produces acid rain.
10. A good surgeon uses a **scalpel** as delicately as a painter uses a brush.
11. The old **cedar** chest in my bedroom is still in good shape.
12. It takes practice to operate a **diesel** engine.
13. The retirement of the company president dealt a **fatal** blow to the business.
14. For the money you spent on that lamp, there had better be a **genie** inside.
15. A **murmur** of disapproval ran through the crowd when someone talked aloud during the dance recital.

ORAL QUIZZES continued

Lesson 17

1. My parents might **disinherit** me if I don't live up to my potential.

2. I skinned my knee, so I put some **antiseptic** on it.

3. We are getting together for our **biannual** festival of the arts.

4. When a new baby arrives, older children sometimes **revert** to infantile behaviors.

5. The steady **accumulation** of snow in the past twelve hours has made it impossible to drive to school.

6. The **monotony** of her job at the fast food restaurant made her decide to quit after two weeks.

7. The meeting was **prearranged,** so I didn't have to call for an appointment today.

8. The doctor's office just called to **confirm** your appointment.

9. My class has such **unity** that we are going to get together over the summer and clean up the old playground.

10. My little brother makes such disgusting noises that I sometimes wonder if he is **subhuman.**

11. I have to **assort** my shorts, slacks, skirts, and dresses before my cousin takes them to her favorite charity.

12. If the author were willing to **condense** this lengthy novel, I would be willing to read it.

13. It can be difficult to travel comfortably when you have a **disability.**

14. The family down the street has to **relocate** because the mother found a new job.

15. You have to be willing to **submerge** your head before you can learn to swim properly.

Lesson 18

1. Alexis worked very hard on her research paper to gain **acceptance** from her teacher.

2. It was **evident** that he failed the test because he had not studied.

3. For some reason, my plan to drive the family car to Florida has met with marked **resistance.**

4. The attorney proved that the **defendant** was out of town the night the crime took place.

5. The professor may be **brilliant,** but brilliance doesn't make him a good teacher.

6. The **radiance** from the street lamp produced a halo of light in the mist.

7. The woman who ran the homeless shelter was also a **prominent** political figure.

8. Myrna was **hesitant** to get in line to have her ears pierced.

9. I know my new employer will want to check at least one **reference** before he allows me to work in the office alone.

10. I had to measure the **circumference** of the lamp to see if it would fit on my desk.

11. He was **ignorant** of the laws governing the tribe, so he offended tribal members without meaning to.

12. One needs determination, education, and practice to become truly **independent.**

13. I decided to purchase some additional **insurance** for my car.

14. The other driver sued her for **negligence** since she was not looking at the road when the accident occurred.

15. A parent of a two-year-old must have plenty of **patience** to deal with the constant question *why.*

ORAL QUIZZES continued

Lesson 19

1. Try to **visualize** how the room will look when it is painted.
2. The Internet continues to **revolutionize** the way that people gather information.
3. We want Howard to **supervise** the project if he is available.
4. If people were willing to **compromise,** many relationships could be saved.
5. It is easier to **criticize** from the sidelines than it is to be part of the game.
6. Daily **exercise** is a key ingredient of good health.
7. We need to **economize** if we are going to save enough money for our trip.
8. The Vegas liked to **socialize** by having friends come to their home for dinner.
9. We are hoping to **organize** a protest against the curfew.
10. The flag is meant to **symbolize** freedom and democracy to Americans.
11. One way to **energize** yourself in the morning is to eat a healthful breakfast.
12. I'm not sure I will **recognize** my best friend after five years apart.
13. I am hoping to **surprise** my mother with a fiftieth-birthday party.
14. At the end of my speech on global warming, I hope to have time to **summarize** my main points.
15. I know she will **sympathize** when I tell her that my neighbor's barking dog has kept me up for the past four nights.

Lesson 20

1. Mrs. Packer asked each student to write a short **biography** of a person who influenced his or her life.
2. Lisa wanted to **transmit** her résumé by e-mail to the company to which she was applying.
3. The **transcript** from the trial was several hundred pages long.
4. The **hydraulic** car lift on the ferry was able to raise twenty cars at a time.
5. If you **persist** in asking me to work for you, I may give in.
6. Brad took a **geology** course to learn about rock formations.
7. Residents near the **missile** base were afraid of potential problems.
8. Her manner was **sophisticated,** but underneath she was shy and lonely.
9. When doctors **prescribe** a medicine, they explain its possible side effects to the patient.
10. Trevor plans to **transfer** to another school next year.
11. The students were taught about **ecology** and how to keep the environment clean.
12. Max could not drive Anita to her lesson because the **transmission** on his car was being repaired.
13. He got a ticket because his car was parked too close to the fire **hydrant.**
14. Geoff's report was **concise,** yet complete.
15. The principal called for an early **dismissal.**

ORAL QUIZZES continued

Lesson 21

1. The **superstition** that warns against walking under ladders has its origin in common sense.

2. Her inability to take **criticism** well caused her problems as a writer.

3. The students showed their **gratitude** to the teacher for his hard work by doing their best on the final exam.

4. Christopher had hoped to go to England next month, but in **reality** he will probably go next year.

5. When she realized that the mouse was a toy, she was even more ashamed of the **cowardice** she had shown.

6. My great-grandfather's pocket knife is my most prized **possession.**

7. The accountant kept the records with such **accuracy** that the company promoted him.

8. His demanding schedule left the **politician** with little time for family life.

9. The task will be easier if there is a **division** of labor.

10. My **optician** stocks the latest styles in glasses.

11. The ancient **civilization** located in that valley was much more advanced than we first thought.

12. Without a positive **attitude,** it is difficult to accomplish very much.

13. The complicated equation could be solved only by a superior **mathematician.**

14. The recent immigrant appreciated the benefits of living in a **democracy.**

15. Mr. Hall's display of **patriotism** was an inspiration to his audience.

Lesson 22

1. Although my mistake on the test seems **laughable** now, at the time I was embarrassed.

2. The **desirable** items at the flea market disappeared quickly, and only junk was left.

3. The **famous** author was asked to be the speaker at graduation.

4. In the lower grades, every attempt is made to teach children how to make their writing **legible.**

5. Because Gordon was an overly **cautious** driver, he attracted glares from other motorists.

6. The house had to be torn down after the fire because the unsupported walls were **dangerous** to passersby.

7. We begged the chef to share her recipe for the **delicious** punch, but the restaurant wouldn't allow her to reveal it.

8. She asked whether it would be **permissible** to leave the wedding reception before the bride and groom's departure.

9. The development of more sophisticated equipment makes most large bodies of water **navigable.**

10. The **horrible** experience of forgetting her lines in the school play made my cousin decide not to be an actress.

11. The **terrible** storm knocked electricity out of hundreds of homes.

12. I am **responsible** for taking the puppy out for his daily walks.

13. Many people found last summer's heat **unbearable.**

14. According to Jeffrey's story, the **furious** winds tore his homework out of his hands, and it disappeared down the street.

15. The guests at the party were surprised at how **spacious** the apartment was.

ORAL QUIZZES continued

Lesson 23

1. The soldiers moved in to **liberate** the prisoners of war.

2. Before leaving, Dr. Johnson needed to **designate** who would be in charge during her absence.

3. Tim felt that the course on American history would **widen** his knowledge of his country's past.

4. "Too little sleep will **stupefy** you," the mother warned her teenage son.

5. The art teacher suggested that Edie **intensify** the blue she was using for the background.

6. Many people planned to **congregate** in the park for the service on Memorial Day.

7. Andrew had to **deepen** the holes he had dug in order to plant the trees properly.

8. The guide told us that some people are not able to **tolerate** the change in altitude at the top of the mountain.

9. Doug keeps pots of water on the radiator in his room to **humidify** the air.

10. Donna needed to **clarify** exactly who was in charge of organizing the parade.

11. The doctor informed her that having the surgery would **heighten** her sense of taste.

12. Working in the soil without wearing gloves will **roughen** the skin of your hands.

13. To **qualify** for the final race, you must win one of four preliminary races.

14. We were told to **circulate** the paper and sign our names if we were interested in participating.

15. Although the sales clerk tried to **glorify** the bracelet, the customer could see by the price that it was not real gold.

Lesson 24

1. In the painting, all of the figures appear to gaze **heavenward.**

2. **Regretfully,** I refused another helping of pie.

3. The lock on the safe had to be turned **clockwise.**

4. This clock chimes **reliably** every quarter of an hour.

5. Because Julie almost always knew the answers, she raised her hand **automatically** when the teacher asked a question.

6. Michael winked at me **knowingly** because we both had heard the joke before.

7. The doctor told Dara that her cat would behave **dully** while recovering from the surgery.

8. Marvin moved **spryly** for a man who had just had a cast taken off his leg.

9. She stacked the tubes **endways** so that they would not roll away.

10. **Ordinarily** our curfew is ten o'clock, but tonight it has been extended.

11. The baby glanced **skyward** when he heard the sound of the jets.

12. Do you think you could **possibly** have this finished by tomorrow morning?

13. Please pay attention; **otherwise,** you will not know what to do.

14. The football player **heartily** ate his way through four courses and then asked for second helpings.

15. The squirrel moved **leisurely** around the garden, pausing to dig up some bulbs and drink from the fountain.

Spelling Power

ORAL QUIZZES continued

Lesson 25

1. The parents agreed that their graduating children looked impressive in their **blue gray** uniforms.
2. When I was a teenager, I enjoyed going to the **drive-in** movies in town.
3. Tanisha has lost **forty-five** pounds on the weight loss plan her doctor recommended.
4. My sister and **brother-in-law** could not attend the family reunion because they had to work.
5. The new soloist was so **self-conscious** that she missed several notes.
6. At eighteen years old, Whiskers is a **long-lived** cat.
7. Yolanda placed her clothes in a **sacklike** bag and pulled the drawstring tight.
8. The managers had to listen to the **tape recording** before they could make their decision.
9. The forklift operator will work at the **warehouse** this summer.
10. I like a **well-done** steak, but my brother prefers his rare.
11. Andrew believes that you can cook if you have a good **cookbook** recipe to follow.
12. I need to take my son to the doctor for a **follow-up** visit just to make sure he is better.
13. My sister gets a **headache** from squinting every time we go to the beach.
14. Marco made the team because he is **self-confident** and also a good hitter.
15. The new employees felt proud to be involved in the company's **decision making.**

Lesson 26

1. The judge announced that the court would take a brief **recess.**
2. The instructions told students to answer the questions on the basis of the **preceding** paragraphs.
3. Although it is **acceptable** to go barefoot at home, you must wear shoes in stores and restaurants.
4. The mother was willing to make one **concession** about school activities as long as her son continued to study.
5. If the demands **exceed** the supply, we will have to charge more for the product.
6. She is such an **exceptional** student that she might be able to start college early.
7. You are less likely to run into trouble if you follow the prescribed **procedure.**
8. The wedding **procession** was longer than any I had seen before.
9. The **receptionist** in the optometrist's office was as polite in person as she was on the phone.
10. I have to go over my accounts **receivable** before I can make additional purchases.
11. Since the graduate student has **access** to the Internet on his computer, he can research at home.
12. Although the advertising campaign was successful, its message was **deceptive** and misleading.
13. Curt thought his brother's routine of exercising for two hours every day was a bit **excessive.**
14. After studying for four years as an undergraduate, I am **proceeding** with my plan to become a veterinarian.
15. The team hit three home runs in rapid **succession,** causing the crowd to go wild.

ORAL QUIZZES continued

Lesson 27

1. Our community celebrates **Mardi Gras** each year with a pancake supper.
2. Doreen is opening a **boutique** that will feature the finest perfumes.
3. My father relaxed on his **chaise longue** while I mowed the lawn.
4. Alan was hoping to marry his **fiancée** before medical school started in the fall.
5. My uncle invited me to his **hacienda** in Mexico for the summer.
6. In Jan's high school, everyone wears jeans or **khaki** pants.
7. On Christmas Eve, her family sings a **noel** around the crackling fire.
8. When Esther returned from her trip to Hawaii, she greeted her family by saying **aloha.**
9. My **tortilla** was so hot that I dropped it, and all of the meat and cheese fell out.
10. Teresa and Paulo rented a **villa** in the south of France for the summer.
11. **En route** to the Grand Canyon, we will stop and visit my mother's best friend.
12. The smallest **llama** at the zoo finally gained weight over the winter.
13. At the local movie theater, the **matinee** is less expensive than the evening show.
14. Before the senior citizens left on their cruise, their families wished them **bon voyage.**
15. My friend Kyle plays **solitaire** on long bus rides to visit his father.

Lesson 28

1. My sister is so **adaptable** that she likes living in Alaska just as well as living in New Jersey.
2. Teachers need to be **rigid** about rules so students will know what is expected of them.
3. Joan has an **optimistic** outlook on life that will serve her well when she joins the Peace Corps.
4. Although Charles is almost certain he failed the test, he is **pessimistic** about the outcome of every test he takes.
5. Her cherry dining set shows her **exquisite** taste in furniture.
6. When Aprille took off the **hideous** mask, her friends were surprised she had played such a scary joke on them.
7. The professor is planning to **integrate** some history lessons into her literature class this year.
8. The teacher wants to **segregate** the younger children from the older ones during recess.
9. Carolyn wasn't sure how to **prevent** reality from intruding on her daydream.
10. The coach tried to **encourage** her to keep practicing even though she had difficulty mastering the swimming strokes.
11. Since Brianna told me to wear **casual** clothes to the dinner party, I was surprised to see Carlos wearing a suit.
12. Renaldo tried not to **cower** before the bully, but he knew Mario was strong.
13. Gene decided to wear his **formal** gray tuxedo to the governor's reception.
14. Since the chef's reputation was excellent, the caterer knew he would be **capable.**
15. The nurse told the patient's mother that her son was so sick that he was **incapable** of hearing her.

ORAL QUIZZES continued

Lesson 29

1. Kevin made an **attempt** to catch the foul ball, but he missed it and fell.

2. Gail was rewarded for her **endeavor** when she received an honorary plaque with her name on it.

3. The actor felt himself **falter** momentarily before making his entrance on stage.

4. It was so hot that Jared did not **hesitate** to jump into the swimming pool as soon as he got home.

5. Unfortunately many people in the city **dwell** in poverty.

6. Someday I would like to **reside** in San Diego, California.

7. He made a **rash** decision, and now he regrets it.

8. **Reckless** driving can lead to disaster.

9. I might feel better if I **eliminate** junk food from my diet.

10. My sister would like to **eradicate** poverty in our town.

11. The restaurant tried to **entice** customers to eat there by offering free dessert with each meal.

12. Denise bought the worms at the bait store, hoping that they would help **lure** a big fish.

13. My father is too **conservative** to wear a loud tie.

14. My mother prefers a **traditional** home.

15. Stacy learned the difficult **maneuver** when she was in basic training.

Lesson 30

1. On the day of Julie's wedding, the **altar** was decorated with pink roses and matching balloons.

2. Joe's new glasses **alter** his appearance.

3. My brother was recently promoted to the rank of **colonel.**

4. Bethany finally told me that I had a **kernel** of corn stuck in my teeth.

5. My grandmother used to make **currant** jelly when I was a child.

6. The game show quizzed its contestants on **current** events.

7. I bought my best friend **stationery** imprinted with her name and address.

8. Riding my **stationary** bicycle is helping me to stay in shape.

9. I wrote only in **capital** letters when I was a preschooler.

10. Congress meets in the **Capitol.**

11. Her **brows** came together in a deep frown whenever she was displeased.

12. The young lady was hoping to **browse** through the store before it closed.

13. I was glad there was a **clause** in the contract that enabled me to terminate the agreement.

14. The **claws** on the cat were so sharp that I hesitated to pet the insistent creature.

15. The fencing coach challenged his student to a **duel.**

ORAL QUIZZES continued

Lesson 31

1. In these model homes, the dining rooms **adjoin** the living rooms.

2. When juries **adjourn** for the afternoon, defendants return to their cells.

3. I can always count on my brother for **moral** support.

4. The coach keeps her team's **morale** high by complimenting them daily.

5. I am worried that too much loud music will **affect** my hearing.

6. The herbal tea had a soothing **effect** on me.

7. The restaurant did not make a **profit** for more than a year.

8. The **prophet** predicted that there would be a new comet discovered in 2010.

9. My aunt believes that teachers do not earn a **decent** salary.

10. The baby began to cry when the plane began its **descent.**

11. It's difficult for a wild animal to **adapt** to life in captivity.

12. I am hoping to **adopt** a pet in the near future.

13. My daughter was so **forceful** in her requests for a new bicycle that I bought one for her birthday.

14. **Forcible** entry into a home or business is against the law.

15. It was my job to **distract** Joseph so that he wouldn't realize we were planning a surprise party for him.

Lesson 32

1. I had to check the baby **monitor** to make sure the newborn wasn't crying.

2. It wasn't **appropriate** to pass out the cookies until the speaker had finished his lecture.

3. Before the voyages of discovery in the sixteenth century, Europeans were unaware of the **existence** of North America.

4. Laura had trouble drawing the curve of the **cylinder.**

5. It was a **coincidence** that the husband and wife both had the same first names.

6. The manual was so **technical** that I put it down in frustration after five minutes.

7. Liz should fill out the **application** for graduate school before summer session starts.

8. Chris was writing a term paper on **nuclear** power for science class.

9. The electrician said **specifically** not to touch the bare wire.

10. Working eighteen-hour shifts causes many medical students to suffer extreme **fatigue.**

11. People have become more concerned about the **environment** in recent years.

12. I was hoping to attend the artist's latest **exhibition,** but I have to work.

13. Sandy had to veer around the **obstacle** in the road to avoid puncturing her tire.

14. Sometimes the **pronunciation** of a foreign word can be difficult.

15. It's Brazil **versus** the United Kingdom in soccer tonight on the sports channel.

Spelling Power